'FROM R

AUTOBIOGRAPHY OF A LAZY COW

With a Foreword by

David Tristram

Flying Ducks Publications

A Flying Ducks paperback

First published in Great Britain

by

Flying Ducks Publications

2014

ISBN 978-1-900997-14-0

For more information on Flying Ducks Publications

visit the website:

www.flyingducks.biz

The Ghost Writer

David Tristram is now one of the country's most popular comedy playwrights. Every single night, on average, there are at least two of his plays being performed somewhere in the world - sometimes in far-flung places like New Zealand, the Vanuatu Islands in the South Pacific, Mexico, Argentina, or Dar Es Salaam - but often in professional and amateur theatres up and down Britain. He's also written a musical, *Sex Drugs & Rick'n'Noel*, a comedy novel, *A Bolt From The Blue*, which would have been a best-seller had it sold more copies, and he's produced two indie movies featuring his cult 1930's character Inspector Drake, which are now available on DVD via the website: www.inspectordrake.com

David's two latest stage works both feature a certain lazy cow.

An Audience With Doreen enjoyed a sell-out tour in 2013-14, and in 2015 she makes a guest appearance in a new satirical one-woman show, *Women On Top*, specially written by David for actress Gill Jordan, who apparently is no relation to Doreen.

David's third movie, currently in production, is simply entitled *Doreen*, though he refuses to say what it's about.

It's due to be completed in 2015 and will be available on DVD, in independent cinemas, and possibly also on local TV.

More details on the movie and the stage shows can be found on Doreen's website: www.doreen.tv

Doreen is a name with Greek origins.

It means "Gift of God"

FOREWORD

By David Tristram

MY AUTOBIOGRAPHY OF SOMEONE ELSE

I don't know when I was born.

Like most people, I was far too young to remember it, and found myself having to rely on the word of others. I've never been a great conspiracy theorist, so I have no reason to imagine that they lied to me, and the consensus, from those who express an opinion, is that it was on the 27th September, 1957.

That makes me quite old. Not as old as some, of course, but much older than I used to be, so I felt instinctively that the time was now right to begin committing my story to paper.

But there was a problem. Looking back at my life, it quickly became apparent that it was nowhere near interesting enough to merit an autobiography. What was I to do? Dull as it was, it was my life, and I could hardly write my autobiography about someone else.

Or could I?

By miraculous coincidence, I then got a call from a man who claimed to represent Doreen Tipton. I'd heard of Doreen, of course - infamous Doreen from 'Doreen's Story', the YouTube clip that went viral with over a million hits virtually overnight. Doreen had been the first woman to be officially diagnosed with Lazy Cow Syndrome, and as a result found herself confined to a life on benefits.

Following the YouTube viral there'd been interest from a TV production company wanting to make a fly-on-the-wall documentary about Doreen, endless requests for interviews from local newspapers and radio stations, and even talk of a stage show and a movie based on her life.

And now, apparently, Doreen was also in need of an autobiography, but of course she was far too lazy to write it herself.

There's nothing new, of course, in the idea of ghost writers 'helping' celebrities to bring their story to the page, and for some reason the agent seemed to believe that I was the right man for the job. I was born and raised in the Black Country, and therefore he argued that I might understand not just Doreen's roots and general philosophy, but also what she said.

I've ghost-written stuff before. The usual method of working is to spend as much time as possible with the subject, to arm yourself with a voice recorder, to interview them on any and all topics, loosen them up, get them chatting, get inside their psyche, and then bring it all together into a coherent story to engage the reader and make them feel that they really know the person.

Could this be the challenge I'd been seeking? My autobiography of someone else?

Perhaps, but I had reservations.

For a start, I found the prospect of getting inside Doreen's mind quite daunting, especially as I tend to suffer from claustrophobia.

Being fairly active around the Black Country, I'd once had the pleasure of meeting Doreen. Actually I'd met her many times, but only once did it give me any pleasure. She lives very near me, and many's the time I've been in the long, snaking queue behind her at the local corner shop, as the cashier processed her bulging basket of Lotto HotPicks, Thunderballs, Euromillions and other assorted scratchcards.

Very occasionally there'd also be an item of food in her basket - a multi-bag of crisps, or jumbo pack of Doritos - but the main food shopping was taken care of by her online delivery from Waitrose. This was paid for, I'm reliably informed, by hacking into someone else's account.

Doreen was no computer genius, so I suspect one of her daughters was to blame. At least that's what the police said when they told me that my Waitrose account had been hacked into.

And so our paths seemed almost fated to cross. I saw the ghost-writing of Doreen's autobiography as a form of victim retribution - a chance to meet the perp, as they insist on calling them in American cop shows (because Americans are too lazy to say the whole word, which presumably is perpendicular, or perplexed, or perhaps even purple, as I've never seen it written down).

So, me and perp, in the same room - her story, my typewriter; her food, my credit card bill. The agent said I would even get paid, eventually. By the state.

I wasn't quite sure how that worked, but I took him at face-value. After all, he had a business card, and an office with a rubber plant. Those things are hard to fake. So I agreed and signed a bit of paper.

Straight away there were logistical issues. I knew

Doreen's work ethic wasn't her strongest point, so the working day as far as I was concerned, explained the agent, had to be confined to the hours between her getting up, and The Jeremy Kyle show being screened in the afternoon - a total of twenty-five minutes. I resolved to make the most of them, but inevitably I feared progress would be painfully slow.

But I was wrong. Gloriously wrong.

The thing is, even though they were only short interviews, Doreen has opinions. About everything. The Government, the Queen, the NHS, the BBC, the Lottery. Inflation, immigration, education, and just about every other 'ation' and Asian you can think of. Yes, this woman has strong opinions. And she's not afraid to express them. So if political correctness is your thing, I'd suggest that you exit quietly now to avoid an incident.

But at least Doreen's opinions made my job easier, and we managed to pack a lot into each session. I just switched on my voice recorder, and she talked. Non-stop. So I scribbled. Non-stop.

Some of Doreen's views, as I say, are not what you might call 'mainstream' these days. Indeed, in the increasingly rarified atmosphere of modern etiquette I fear that some people might even find her views 'offensive', much as I find people who take offence too easily offensive. But they are her views. And, I suspect, they are the views of many like her. And perhaps many not so like her. So we neglect them at our social peril.

I learned such a lot in a very short time about this extraordinary woman. And along the way there were other little unexpected gems. She had the sort of vocabulary that would have made Mrs Malaprop blush. Why use two words when one wrong one will suffice? I decided not to correct them in the final draft - they are an essential part of her character, and in a weird sense they almost add to the meaning, rather than detract from it. So what if she does say 'cholesterol' instead of 'collateral'? Or 'locusts' instead of 'locums'? Or 'posthumous' instead of 'promiscuous'? We know what she meant. And in the end that's all we need from a language. To know. To understand.

Just for the record, I also chose not to try and write Doreen's story in some kind of phony phonetic Black Country dialect, which I always think looks really naff on the page. Just a hint here and there in reported speech, yes, but mainly it's in the Queen's English (or nearest offer).

So by all means watch Doreen's Story on YouTube and then try to imagine the accent for yourself when reading the book, but I decided not to force the issue by writing 'day' instead of 'didn't', or 'ay' instead of 'aren't', or 'gooing' instead of 'going'. I thought that may get tiresome very quickly. Besides, the dialect is not the point. It's the thoughts and the person behind them that really count.

In the end, of course, you will make up your own mind about Doreen. But as far as I was concerned, something extraordinary happened in our brief time together.

This woman - how she lives, how she thinks, her views, her expectations, her total mind-set - is about as far from me and my philosophy of life as it's possible to get. And yet I inevitably came away with a smile. In fact, I came away with more than a smile.

I came away liking Doreen.

Yes, I liked her a lot.

And, unfashionable as it may be, I shared some of her angst.

David Tristram

PART ONE

SYNDROMES, FAMILY & FRIENDS

CHAPTER ONE
DOCTOR'S ORDERS

It all started when the doctor put me on a double dose of that Dimarzipan, on account of my restless legs.

"The best thing to do with restless legs," he said, "is to rest them." So naturally I put my feet up whenever I could. And one thing led to another.

By the time I was twenty I was on loads of drugs - heroin, crack, Fentanyl, Rohypnol…that's the date rape drug, Rohypnol. Bloody hopeless. I was on that for six months and no bugger came near me.

But it didn't stop there. Amphetamines, Ketamine, Opium, Ritalin, Crystal Meth, Xodol, Zydone, wacky baccy, a gallon of diesel, Windolene, Brasso, Bostik - you name it, I've tried them all. I even had a go with one of them new designer drugs. I think it was called Crack by Armani.

For the next eighteen months I was at the medical centre so often that they offered me a job as the receptionist. But I turned it down. I didn't feel it was the right time to make important career choices.

I saw doctors come and go – three of them either left or retired in the first month, stating me as the reason, and two young ones arrived straight out of medical school who looked about eleven, so I gave them a wide birth. Then there was a woman doctor. She just frowned a lot and only seemed interested in asking questions.

"I don't need any bloody questions," I told her. "It's answers I want."

Eventually they tried to flob me off by referring me to some therapist, by which they meant some sort of brain specialist. They reckon now that about half of all mental conditions are just in the head, so they try and send you to see a therapist rather than a proper doctor. It was another waste of time. I only saw him the once and then he was off with depression. It was him who reckoned I was probably bi-focal, the same as that Stephen Fry. Apparently it's a condition that normally afflicts intelligent folk. It's all down to thinking too much.

Things did finally seem to be looking up though when I got a phone call from the medical centre saying they was going to refer me to a specialist in Harley Street.

At last, I thought, they're finally taking it seriously.

So I popped into the doctors the next day to ask for some petty cash for the train fare to London and the taxis. It's not cheap down there. But I came back empty-handed. It seems I'd misheard the phone call. The so-called specialist was in Hardy Street, which is in Stoke-on-Trent.

Now, I don't know if you've ever been to Stoke, but most of it has been knocked down now, and the only way to get to some bits of it is by canal boat, which takes about three months. My next-door neighbour, Jack (you'll meet him soon) used to joke that if Stoke-on-Trent had been totally destroyed in the war they would have done about twenty pounds worth of damage.

He went up to do a quick plumbing job there once and he came back saying "Never again!" Jack had quoted fifty quid for fitting a tap, apparently, and the bloke had said no because he'd only paid forty for the house. And even then, Jack reckoned this bloke must have paid well over the market value.

Anyway, I reasoned that any brain specialist worth

his salt wouldn't set up shop in Stoke, even though there must be plenty of business up there for him, and I also struggle with some of the dialect that far north, so in the end I cancelled the appointment and told them I wanted something a bit more local.

So then it was back to the next doctor in the queue, and he'd already cancelled three appointments with me, so I was starting to get suspicious. They told me that he was off long-term sick, which is odd because I saw his car on the car park.

Then I asked to see the doctor who'd signed the other doctor off long-term sick, because I thought I needed a similar diagnosis, but they said he'd now gone private, and it would cost me a hundred and forty quid for ten minutes. Looking back, I think they were giving me the runaround. In the end I had to agree to see one of them stand-in doctors - locusts they call them. And it turned out he was foreign, so that was no good either.

Finally, after getting my neighbour Doris (you'll meet her as well soon) to write me a letter to the local MP, I got a note back saying they were going to fast-track me to the hospital. That took four years. Four years to get fast-tracked. And where did I end up? Stafford. I'm lucky I lived to tell the tale.

But that's the NHS for you. You get what you pay

for. That's you and me paying for that, out of our taxes. Well, your taxes, my benefits, whatever. They get it out of us somehow.

Anyway, I suppose it all turned out for the best in the long-run, because the hospital specialist spotted it straight away. And so then he did all the tests, and he said - and I shall never forget his words - he said:

"Mrs Tipton, I'm afraid it's confirmed. You're a lazy cow."

Well, of course, that came as no real shock to me, because my mother had it, and there's a good chance I shall pass it on to my kids, because it's genetic.

That was over twenty years ago, and there's been a lot of water under the canal since. I have good days and bad. Mainly bad. And the good days aren't very good either. So on reflection I suppose I have bad days and not very good days. I've spent the best part of twenty years in and out of NHS waiting rooms doing exactly what it said on the sign - waiting. But even today, after all the therapy, I still have trouble shifting my arse.

I have to say, though, getting the proper Lazy Cow diagnosis after all those years was a big relief for me because, well, the first lot of doctors, they hadn't got a clue, quite frankly. I'm sure they just thought I was malinjering.

But that was back in the nineties, and they're a lot more enlikened now that we're in the 20th century. They're learning more and more about syndromes, inventing new ones every day. But Lazy Cow is still one of the worst, because to the untrained eye the symptoms aren't easy to spot.

In the early stages it can look very much like other conditions, such as rigor mortis. In later life, it can develop and affect different parts of your body, and if you're a sufferer you never know where it's going to strike next - wrist, legs, back - some days nothing works.

A few years ago the taxi pulled up sudden on the way to the Job Centre, and I got a bad case of that whipcrack on the neck. The doctor gave me the antibiotics, but it's never been right since. It ended up costing the taxi company a lot of money, because apart from the physical and mental trauma I also had to claim for loss of earnings - that's the earnings I would have had if I'd managed to get a job good enough to make it worthwhile me giving up the benefits for.

They paid up in the end when I got one of them personal injury lawyers involved. He was a nice chap with very shiny shoes, a pin-striped suit and a really unusual name - McShitehawke. He told me to tell the taxi lawyers that I kept having black-outs and that I might eventually lose the sight of one eye because of a semi-detached rectum. As it happens, I was experiencing occasional black-outs at the time, but I thought that was more to do with the amount of brandy I was drinking because of the stress, and I hadn't noticed anything wrong with my eye at that point. Anyway, in the end the taxi lawyers forced me to go and have a proper medical exhumation.

To my surprise, the doctor ended up confirming the eye problem to the taxi company's lawyers and they eventually coughed up, though they refused to pay cash. It stuck in my mind at the time, because the examining doctor was also called McShitehawke, and I remember saying to one of the kids "What are the chances of that?"

Over the years, Lazy Cow Syndrome has been like a rollercoaster for me, without the ups. Yes, being the first to be officially diagnosed with it was a big honour in some ways, but then I was under the spotlight a bit, and folks with a natural tendency to be a bit less energetic looked to me for leadership. I felt under pressure not to let them down, and that took its toll on me physically. Some days, just getting out of bed was a triumph. Other days it wasn't. So I didn't.

There's no doubt, it's been a battle. Now I know how those soldiers must have felt coming back from places like Iraq, and other parts of the Middle Ages. Post dramatic stress disorder, they call it. That's one of them new syndromes, and it's no laughing matter. I've read up on some of the symptoms, and it's just how I feel when I see a hoover.

Throughout my long ordeal though, I've been very lucky to have had such tremendous support from my neighbours, Doris and Jack.

It's time to meet them.

CHAPTER TWO
DORIS AND JACK

Doris is my ironing lady, and she really deserves a chapter all to herself. But I couldn't mention Doris without mentioning Jack, and Jack's probably not worth a chapter on his own, so they'll have to share.

Doris is absolute pillow of the community, and I owe her a huge debt of ingratitude. She's been my next-door neighbour ever since she moved in next door, about twenty years ago, and she got to hear about my syndrome when I told her about it the first time we met. Ever since then she's popped in on a Monday and a Thursday to do the ironing. And on a Wednesday to help with the washing. And the hoovering. And on the other days she just pops in to see if I need anything doing around the house. She's as good as gold. She'll even cook a few meals for me if I want her to, and usually I do.

But as well as being work colleagues, Doris and I are also good friends. We see hand-in-hand on most issues, and when we start putting the world to rights there's no stopping us - politics, religion, bankers, foreigners, the NHS, Jeremy Kyle - all the big issues of the day, sorted.

We're also both, in our own very different ways, real grafters. With Doris it's more physical - she's always on the go - whereas with me it's more of a thought process. All successful armies need generals and foot-soldiers, and that's how it is with us. Doris would always be the first one to jump into the trench and roll her sleeves up for you, while I'm more of a strategist, giving out the orders. I'm Napoleon to her bony parts, and that's how we've managed to get so much done together over the years.

Without Doris, I really don't know how I would have coped. But this syndrome is even starting to take its toll on her. She works nights as a cleaner at the local shoe factory in Sedgley, sometimes doing double shifts and triple shifts to make ends meet, so by the time she has to start my housework she's shattered. On one occasion she had to cover for three of her workmates who were either off sick or on holiday. One was off sick and on holiday at the same time. It meant she did a quadruple shift - a thirty-two hour day. She was still there the following morning and not able to do her proper shift because the times overlapped, so then somebody had to cover for her. Course, that meant that the one who was covering for Doris couldn't then do her own shift later that day, so Doris had to cover for her. It was nearly eleven o'clock when she finally got in the next night, and she was so shattered I told her to leave the ironing for a bit while she made me a cup of tea.

I've told her - she needs to think of herself more, to get her priorities right. Money's not everything. She should book some time off from the factory. She's no good to me in that state. But she says she can't afford any time off at the moment, because she's so busy she's having to pay someone to come in and do her ironing. So she's in a bit of a Catch 69 situation.

And of course, when she's finally finished all her chores here, Doris has to go and cook Jack's tea.

Jack is Doris's husband.

Jack's a good bloke, even though he was originally from across the border in Birmingham. Brummies don't normally mix too well with us Black Country folk - we have very different cultures and languages, and try as you might you can't force ethnics to get on if they don't understand each other. Ironically, though, the Government now seem to like us being multi-functional, so in the modern world I reckon they'd approve of Doris and Jack inter-breeding. In fact you can probably get a grant for it these days.

But that sort of thing wasn't around when they got married in the eighties, and I know it caused a lot of ill-feeling at the time. In those days, the Brummies and the Yam-Yams (that's what they called us) were segregated, like the whites and blacks were when Nelson Mandelson was in charge in South America. We got on different buses, went to different schools. In fact, it was because we went to different schools that we got on different buses. Doris tells me her dad wouldn't even speak to Jack at first, not until he agreed to renounce his religion and converted to the Wolves. He also had to learn to stop saying things like 'barth' instead of 'bath'.

"There's no bloody R in it, yer poncey bugger," her dad would say. I've since looked it up, and he was right.

Doris and Jack never had kids. Doris told me that it was all to do with Jack's bits and pieces. They'd had him tested at the clinic because he was incompetent, and it turned out that his pipes were a bit blocked up, which isn't very good for a plumber. Anyway, the long and short of it was that Jack apparently hadn't got enough sperm. But that sounds a bit fishy to me, because you only need one. I reckon the real reason they didn't have kids was to do with the prejudice at the time. It would have been a tough upbringing for a mixed-race Brum-Yam kid back then. You have to remember, these were the eighties, when there was no such thing as gay people, or health and safety, when mobile phones were slightly bigger than phone boxes, when everybody wanted to be in the same gang as Gary Glitter, and it was okay to call Indians darkies. Of course, we're all a lot more enlikened now, since the Labour Party started letting all sorts in. It's just one giant melting pot round by us now, and nobody bats an eyeball these days if you say you're going out with somebody from Small Heath. But in those days it was voodoo, and anybody that broke the rules could face being ostrichised or, worse still, sent to Coventry, which apparently is even further south than Birmingham.

As I mentioned before, Jack's a plumber by trade, though his business is really suffering badly at the minute. I don't want to point any fingers, but it's all them Polish plumbers. They're everywhere. In fact I think my dentist's one as well. He's certainly not from round here, and I've heard stories of him using a monkey wrench on people's teeth.

Now, it's one thing letting in the Brummies, quite another being invaded by Poland. That's how the Second World War started, if I remember my history lessons correctly, and we should never forget the lessons of history. I'm not very good with dates, but I'm pretty sure that Poland invaded Hitler, and it all kicked off after that. The problem is, I know these Poles probably mean well, but for a start-off they're apparently quite industrious, which doesn't go down very well round here, and they keep on undercutting Jack on price and nicking all his work.

That's something else the Government's got to sort out. It's all very well getting in cheap foreign labour to undercut on price, but they just haven't got the skills of the British workers. Jack was an apprentice plumber before most of them foreigners were out of whatever the Polish version of nappies is, and he knows how to wield a hammer. He fixed the hot dripping tap in my kitchen in a jiffy. Two smacks, it was done. No more drips. He also advised me not to use the tap again - I doubt the foreigners offer that sort of free professional advice - but the cold tap still works, and I can always boil a kettle, or get Doris to do it for me, so no real damage done.

Jack's what I call a good old-fashioned traditional British craftsman. For a start he's dependable. When he says he's not going to turn up, he means it. And he's also not the sort to rush a job. He weighs it up first over a few cups of tea, gives a few sharp intakes of breath, and then goes and sits in his van having a bacon sandwich for half an hour. When he does finally get cracking, nine times out of ten he hits a snag, because whoever it was who did the job before him was a cowboy, and it takes him ages to sort out the mess they left.

Yes, Jack's a good bloke, as steady as a rock. And no funny business with other women either. No, not Jack. They've been married over thirty years and I don't think I've ever heard Jack raise his voice once. In a nutshell, he's the absolute salt of the hearth, and you couldn't wish for a nicer bloke.

Mind you, he can also be a bit of a boring bastard sometimes.

He keeps going on about how he can "save up to eleven percent of fuel by driving at exactly fifty-six miles an hour, dependent, of course, on the nature of the terrain." And then there's his hobby, studying and reciting washing machine instruction booklets. He's got to learn that we're not all as interested in that sort of thing as he is.

But Jack's a good bloke, and Doris is lucky to have him. Lucky to have each other really.

Good neighbours are very important when you live on your own. Apart from Doris and Jack, I also rely on Bernard from two doors down. Despite him being eighty-seven and having one lung, plastic hips and three fingers missing, Bernard still comes to cut my lawn every week, rain or shine. He's also offered on more than one occasion to trim my bush, but I prefer Doris to wax it. Actually, I think I'm right in saying that Bernard lost his three fingers while he was trimming somebody else's bush, so I'm surprised he offered.

I have to ask Doris to let him run the cable for his lawnmower over the fence to her house, because my electricity bill's a nightmare, but she doesn't mind.

Doris, you see, is working, so it's easier for her to pay the bills, whereas I have to rely on the benefits. And the more money that people like me need to live on welfare, the more likely it is that they'll start taxing Doris more, so it helps her out in the long run.

Apart from a bit of help from the neighbours, I pretty much have to fend for myself.

Now some of you who already know me might be wondering why I've got this far into the story - introduced you to myself, Doris and Jack, even Bernard the gardener - and not yet mentioned my kids. Well, to be honest, it's partly because I forgot about them. You see, for reasons you'll discover as the tale unfolds, they no longer live with me, so out of sight, out of mind. But they are an important part of my life, so I will be devoting a whole chapter to them in a bit.

According to police records, I've got three kids. There's Trojan (our Troje), Tangerine (our Tange), and Trollop (our Troll), and all of them in their own unique way have left their mark. That's especially true of Trojan, my first-born, who left her mark right up my stomach when she had to be delivered by Bavarian section. Apparently, according to the midwives, she tried to strangle herself with the umbicular cord just before she was born, possibly on purpose.

The doctors said it was a miracle Trojan survived, although there's plenty that wouldn't see it that way. Don't get me wrong, I wouldn't be without her, even though I am, but she was a proper handful. I wish I'd have had a zip put on my stomach though rather than being stitched up, because the second kid came out the other way, and Christ it hurt. They tried me on gas and air at first, but eventually I was screaming so much they put me on morphine and heroin. I still reckon that's how I ended up being afflicted to drugs, even though it wasn't the first time I'd had them. Apparently, not even that did the trick, so in the end the big black midwife lost her temper and punched me out cold. This worked well. I was very grateful to her afterwards, and we still keep in touch. When I came round they placed our Tangerine in my arms, we looked at each other, and we both started crying.

For the third one, Troll, the hospital was a bit more organized. They'd already decided to put me on a general anaesthetic, but they also had the big black midwife on stand-by in case that didn't work out.

As it happened Troll was a much easier birth for me, as I was unconscious at the time, except they were a bit worried at first because I didn't come round for three days. Doris had to explain that this was normal.

Anyway, I didn't want to get into all this now.

There'll be a chapter on the kids soon. But first, I need to explain how I make my living.

CHAPTER THREE

AN HONEST DAY'S BENEFITS

Every Wednesday I have to go to the Job Centre.

Public transport's not an option for me. I used to have to catch the bus, but the nearest bus stop is over fifty yards away from my house, so that's something else the Government's got to sort out. And I found when I was running for the bus that I was tripping on a lot of uneven pavements, which was costing the council a lot of money. So the private taxi works out much cheaper for them.

I've got my own dedicated counsellor now at the Job Centre. He's a smarmy old bugger.

"Can I remind you, Mrs Tipton," he says, "that this particular part of your benefits is called Job Seeker's Allowance. The idea is that you actually seek a job."

He must think jobs grow on trees. My financial adviser said that once you take into account the income tax, the national insurance, the free house, the council tax benefit, the child benefit, disability allowance, the job seeker's and a few other bits and pieces, it's not worth me taking a job that pays less than £127,000 a year. That means I would need to wait until the leader of the local council resigns, and then put in my CV. Not that I've got a CV. The Job Centre did make me put one together once, but when they looked at it they decided I'd have more chance of getting a job without one.

There was a bit of a rumpole about it all recently. It came about when they decided to do a review of my circumstances. They just can't leave well alone. They seemed surprised that I was getting jobseekers, disability benefit and working tax credit at the same time. Apparently it's unusual. I don't see why. I still have to look for a job - their rules - even if I'm not fit to do it, and I may not have been paid enough to do the job that I can't do and haven't found anyway, so I need the working tax credit to help make ends meet.

Then they started talking about putting me on the new Universal Credit - up to £26,000 a year tax-free. Well, at first I thought it was a reasonable offer, until I realized, while they were giving that with one hand, they were trying to take away the rest of my benefits with the other. Crafty buggers. They must think I was born yesterday. So I went straight up the Citizens Device Bureau. My lawyers are on to it now.

What a lot of people don't realize is that claiming benefits is a job in itself. It's a lot harder than it looks. There are questions to answer, forms to get Doris to fill in, and so on. And then with, like, the disability benefit, you need to bear in mind that they might come and assess you without notice. They've even got them long lens cameras now, so I find that I have to wear the neck-brace all the time when I'm out, which isn't good for my neck, and I've taken to keeping the curtains shut in the daytime, just in case there's any of those Peperami photographers about.

I also don't think they realize that getting over to the Job Centre really disrupts your week. They want me there now at half-past two on the dot, so I have to skip breakfast. These days I'm never back on a Wednesday before three o'clock, and I do like to be around to keep an eye on Doris. Don't get me wrong, Doris is no slacker, but it's only human nature to work just that bit slower when nobody's looking.

Anyway, they said that unless I applied for three jobs a week, they were going to stop my benefits. I reminded him that the specialist had said that I wouldn't ever work again, but they didn't seem impressed.

And it isn't like I haven't tried.

I applied to be a vet, but they made a big fuss about me needing all sorts of qualifications. Apparently, having a cat doesn't count. It was the same with the dentist's job, despite me having teeth. I also applied to be an HGV truck driver, even though I wasn't sure what one was, and I actually got an interview for that, but I still didn't get the job. No way.

First question out of his mouth: "Can you drive?"

I told him straight, and the interviewer bloke just lost interest after that. It's because I'm a woman, you see. I don't think my lack of driving experience really came into it, because at the end of the day that can be taught, whereas being a woman, well you're generally stuck with that from birth, unless you decide to apply to the NHS to have one of them new trans-bender operations. I'm sorry, but there's no way I'm having a willy sewn on just to get a job as a truck driver.

And that's the thing - all these employers now are prejudiced against the likes of me. They're only after people who've got something to offer, which just isn't fair to the rest of us.

I've stopped doing interviews now, because it's the same wherever you go. The moment you tell an employer you don't want the job, they just seem to lose interest.

If you ask me, there's no real point chasing work anyway. Everybody knows there aren't enough jobs to go round, so if you think about it, you're not doing the country any favours by taking one of them. It's just common sense - if there's a shortage of work, the jobs ought to go to them that needs the money the most, not the ones on welfare.

Government policy backs this up. The politicians must favour welfare over work. Why else would they tax work, but leave benefits tax-free? They just won't rest until we're all on benefits, and they've got us right where they want us.

And the Job Centre's more of a hindrance than a help. They want me up there once a week now, which in itself stops me from being able to take on a full-time job, so they haven't really thought that through either have they?

I do wonder sometimes though if they really want me to get a job at all. Where's the incentive? After all, if they managed to get jobs for all the people like me, they'd be left with no customers. That would presumably mean they'd be out of a job themselves, so then they'd have to open up a special Job Centre just for ex Job Centre staff to attend. And I suppose that would need staffing, so then they might have to take some of them back on again. It's all very confusing. Much easier to keep things how they are, with them working and me claiming.

At the end of the day, the Government recognizes that benefits claimants are a vital part of the public sector. My accountant explained it to me like this. Benefits claimants generate wealth by spending money on scratchcards and other stuff, which in turn generates tax revenue from the private companies that make the stuff. That tax money is used to spend on our benefits. So, if everybody worked, there'd be less need to tax people, so then they'd be better off, and have less incentive to work hard, which would cause the economy to collapse as they all fell into idleness.

I see it as my job to keep those in employment on their toes, fighting to make a living for all of us.

Not that I need a job. I've got lots to keep me busy. It's all about self-discipline, and planning your day. For a start, anybody who's got too much free time on their hands is obviously getting up too early. I'll admit I'm not a morning person. I am sometimes an afternoon person, like on a Wednesday, but not by choice. I tend to peak about five o'clock, and I'm pretty much alert then and on the go right through till seven, unless it's a Tuesday. With the Job Centre visit looming the next day I usually try and have an early night, but it's not always possible if, for example, Doris is behind with the ironing and I have to gee her up a bit. That's the pattern mid-week, but obviously things are different at weekends.

Doris comes round about seven or eight times a week now, what with the ironing, and the hoovering and the washing and the dusting and the cooking to do, and she can talk for England. It's a wonder she ever gets anything done. So obviously I have to keep her company and give her some moral support - it's quite time-consuming for me, but I think it would be rude just to leave her to it. And the way the telly is these days, with the Sky catch-up and the Freeview, it's possible to settle down and watch the entire season of Jeremy Kyle back-to-back in one session, with the adverts just giving Doris enough time to boil the kettle. So to be honest, there's never enough hours in the day, and how anybody thinks I could manage a job on top of all that lot is beyond me. Doris agrees with me. The only way she manages to fit it all in herself is to work nights, which is no good for me because that's generally when I'm asleep.

Job or no job, it's a real struggle for me lately, and I sometimes wonder how it's all going to end. I've just heard on the news that they're putting up the retirement age again. They reckon we'll all have to work till we're seventy. And I bet by the time I'm seventy, it'll be up to eighty. Trouble is, I really can't see me going up that Job Centre until I'm eighty. And that's another social injustice. Working folk shouldn't be the only ones who are allowed to retire. My only hope of putting my feet up is to get a job when I reach retirement age, and then immediately retire from it.

But in the meantime, I have to put up with the smarmy counsellor once a week. He just doesn't see the bigger picture. Last week he finally lost patience with me and said, "Look, Mrs Tipton, you've got to take whatever we give you, all right? You've got to be prepared to take on the most lowly, unskilled, poorly-paid, embarrassing, demeaning job, no matter what it is."

So here I am, selling my story.

CHAPTER FOUR
MY ROOTS ARE SHOWING

Some years back I asked the kids to look into the geology of our family tree on one of those online ancestral websites.

I wanted to know the full history of the condition I was facing. What was Lazy Cow? Was it something that could be easily passed on from mother to child? Was it an airborne virus that could be inhaled while yawning? Would any or all of my daughters be cursed with the same terrible affliction? Was it triggered by some single tragic event? Sometimes I would lie awake for minutes thinking about these things, and I sensed that the answers lay buried somewhere in my family history.

The kids didn't get very far on the computer,

because after a few seconds they were asked to provide a credit card, so in the end we decided just to use some good old-fashioned detective work.

My mother, Ethel, was the easiest member of the family to track down, because she was living in my spare room at the time. But getting information out of her wasn't going to be that easy. She was only sixty-two then, but already showing signs of early on-site feline dementia, and her short-term memory wasn't good. Like a lot of old demented sufferers, though, her long-term memory was vivid, so when I asked her a question about the family history I could tell she knew the answer. The problem was, she kept forgetting what the question was.

Eventually, we did manage to piece together some of the facts.

It was the late fifties, an era of high fashion, when the Black Country was considered the place to be. One rainy Saturday night my mother, Ethel Bertha Tipton, had met an Irish navvy called Seamus in a pub at Wednesbury - The Cock & Scratchings. He'd come over on a ferry looking for work, but ended up getting my mother pregnant and staying the night, in that order.

That set the pattern. He never got a job, and they never got married, because Seamus didn't turn up at the church. At least, mother didn't think he turned up, but she couldn't be sure, because she didn't turn up either. Things were different in those days.

Anyway, one morning, just a few months into their relationship, Seamus disappeared without trace, and mother miscarried two days later after accidentally swallowing eight pints of stout.

Stout was the tipple of choice for sophisticated men and women in those days. For some reason it's less popular now, except in Ireland, where Seamus came from, but it used to be good for you. Even the television adverts said so, though probably they meant in quantities of less than a gallon a time, and not so much when you're pregnant.

Anyway, mother eventually got back on her feet, and then back off her feet and back onto her back, as there followed a whole string of liaisons with other shadowy gentlemen, one of whom presumably was my father. Mother never talked about my father. He was just another one of the voodoo subjects in our house. She wouldn't even tell me his name, though I'm sure she would have if she could. Much like me, she never had any luck with men. That's why I keep telling Doris she's so lucky to have Jack, regardless of how boring he is. The men in our household just came and went, as it were. And along the way they left behind four other kids as well - all daughters.

I had more ugly step-sisters than Cinderella.

In many ways, my mother was an amazing woman. Being able to bring up five kids in those days while at the same time not holding down a job, that was a remarkable achievement. I remember when I was a young girl I always perspired to be like my mother. And in a sense, I suppose I did eventually follow her career path.

Just in case you're wondering, I have no idea what became of my four step-sisters. I was the youngest, so what little memory I have of them is now faded. They had all left home by the time I was four, the judge having awarded custody in each case to the absent drunk father.

Looking back, it's obvious to me now that mother carried the gene, or possibly the pair of genes, responsible for Lazy Cow Syndrome. Of course, back in those days there wasn't the welfare support structure for victims that there is now. If the washing or ironing needed doing, there was no Government money for home help, you just had to get off your backside and find someone else to do it for you.

My mother was very good at this. Her next-door neighbour, Eunice, was a God-send - a bit like my Doris. Mother never had to lift a finger. Ironing, washing, cooking - Eunice catered for Ethel's every need. Monday to Sunday, she'd pop in hourly, and stay about sixty minutes each time.

Only in later life did it become clear that Eunice did this not so much out of sheer neighbourly kindness, but guilt.

It was many years before mother discovered that when Seamus had left her and disappeared without trace he'd actually gone next-door. Eunice, after all, was a far better cook, by virtue of the fact that she occasionally did some cooking, and she managed to keep Seamus in the style in which he wanted to become accustomed.

Indeed, his new whereabouts might never have been discovered were it not for the fateful night when Seamus came back from the pub so drunk that he slipped into the wrong house, and the wrong bed, and the wrong woman. Mother, unusually for her, actually woke up during the foreplay, and said she would have screamed for help if she'd known it was Seamus. But the lights were off, and she'd assumed it was just a total stranger.

Seamus, for all his other faults, was as fertile as a racehorse. Mother miscarried once again, this time after only six pints of stout, but the secret was out and the damage was done.

Ethel and Eunice never spoke again.

They continued to swap washing baskets in total silence.

Despite their feud, mother was devastated when Eunice died. I dare say Eunice herself was none too pleased, but if anything it hit mother even harder, because she had to witness the tragedy. The month before, Seamus had got Eunice to pack his bags, and had moved out and into the next terraced house down, enticed by Mrs Peterson's dumplings. Eunice had never got over the shock. She passed away peacefully when, suffering from guilty self-neglect and malnutrition, she fainted at mother's ironing board, pulling the hot iron down onto her own head.

I was actually there that day, playing in the garden. I remember hearing the bang, followed by a hissing noise, and mother's swear words. In her more lucid moments, mother still recounts the dreadful horror of that day - how there was still nearly half a basket of ironing to do, and how she had to pull the chicken out of the oven herself.

Even though I was only a little girl at the time, I still remember it vividly, albeit slightly differently. When you're just twelve years old, you don't forget something like that - being instructed to finish the ironing and take a chicken from an oven.

It affected me psychopathically, and though I didn't

know it at the time, I would never be able to face housework again.

That was all a long time ago, but the scars run deep. The doctors and mentalists have all done their best, though most of them were a total waste of time, but things are no further forward.

Deep down, I know that Lazy Cow Syndrome is a life sentence. Mother's the living proof. She never recovered.

About fifteen years ago she had a nasty fall, and has never been the same since. She tripped on one of the kids' roller skates at the top of the stairs, and after that she went downhill fast.

She broke her collarbone in two places - in the kitchen and in the garden. And from that day forth she never lifted a finger to help around the house. I just thought the sparkle had gone out of her eyes. The doctor said it was cataracts, but I could tell she'd lost her joy-de-vile. It was almost like she'd died inside. It certainly smelled like that.

Reluctantly, about ten years ago, I had to have her sectioned and moved into a reinforced care home. The penile dementia had got worse, and looking after her was just getting too much for Doris.

I'd heard horror stories of people having to sell

their houses to pay for care, so I was glad mine was rented and paid for by the state. It's a strange thing about the system in this country, but the best way to make sure someone can't take away your home is not to own it.

Despite all that, mother's still going strong, bless her cotton urine-stained socks. I try to remember to go and visit her every three or four years, but because of her condition I'm like a stranger to her. It's worth persevering though, because she once let out that she'd stashed some money somewhere, and I've never found it. The care home workers have said that the in-mates can occasionally have lucid flashbacks, so you never know.

I've got to say as well, those care home workers are absolutely marvellous, and I for one don't begrudge them occasionally using mild violence. I certainly couldn't do their job. Or any job for that matter. They've got such endless patience, even when mother tells them to fuck off. She doesn't mean it. It's all part of being demented, apparently.

I'm told she regresses back to her childhood, when she used to have Turrets, which is that swearing disease, named after something to do with a castle. That's yet another syndrome. In our day it was just called having a foul mouth.

Actually, on second thoughts, knowing mother, she probably does mean it. She's always had a foul mouth on her, and she hates anybody in uniform.

Anyway, that's just a bit about the history of my family tree and its roots, and it gives you a bit of a hindsight into my childhood upbringing. I thought that by showing you where I came from, it would help you see where I'm coming from.

In the next chapter, however, we will start to look forward rather than back, to the next generation - the future of this country.

My children.

CHAPTER FIVE
TROJAN, TANGERINE AND TROLLOP

The best advice I could offer anyone raising kids, is not to have them in the first place.

I mean, don't get me wrong, I wouldn't be without my kids, my little rug-rats, and to be fair they have helped bring in a bit of income over the years. But just between you and me, there have been times when I've said to myself that if I could shove them back where they came from I would. And I know all the mothers reading this today would feel the same, because kids are basically nothing but a pain.

I wouldn't ever say it to their faces though, because I know they're a bit sensitive and they might take it the wrong way. In fact, the only reason I said it here is because I know that my kids would never dream of reading a book.

But having said that, I'm really just like any other mother: once you realize you're stuck with the little buggers, the maternal instinct kicks in, and you just want what's best for them. Of course, for a woman in my position, that's not always possible.

People think that folk on benefits have all the latest gadgets - phones and plasmas and stuff.

It's not true.

No disrespect, but some people just have no idea how it makes you feel, as a devoted mother, to see your youngest daughter come home from truancy, distraught, crying her little eyes up, throwing things around the room, smashing up the crockery, because her friend Jade, who after all only works on the checkout at Aldi, has the latest iPhone 5s, with 4G, and 64 gig memory and a nice bundle of apps, while my daughter, who has no real prospect of any taxable income, has to make do with a six-month-old i-Phone 5c.

And the telly - folks always joke about the likes of us having huge plasmas, but it's just another myth. I never went for the ninety-inch in the end, because it would have meant moving a load-bearing wall, and I didn't want Doris to have the mess. On top of that, the council wouldn't give me planning permission.

The kids also went mad at me to have one of them 3D tellies for Christmas, but I said to them, "What's the point - you've only got two eyes, ay yer?"

I had to put me foot down. I told them they'd got to wait until the January sales, because it's all about priorities. But inside I felt bad about depriving them.

As a responsible mother, my main concern has always been putting food on the table every night. Okay, the takeaway bloke brings it to the door, but I still have to put it on the table, because once he's had his cash he washes his hands of it. And that in a nutshell is the big problem with employed folk these days - nobody's got a pride in their work any more.

But I have to say, despite all that, just because you're brought up in poverty, it doesn't mean you can't be a happy, loving family. Family values have always been very important to me. There's nothing I used to like more than just a quiet night in, gathered round the plasma with my daughters, watching my favourite film, The Railway Kids.

In so many ways, the railway kids remind me of us. They were poor as well, having to make do with hand-me-downs, just like the old i-Phones my kids have got. And the father, he was also absent, just like here. In prison. Though in the film I think he was innocent.

I don't think I've ever watched that film and not cried at the scene at the end, where the dad comes back from prison on the steam train and the eldest kid shouts:

"Daddy! My daddy!"

Gets me every time. Mind you, if that happened to us, it would probably be a bit different. Our Trojan would probably catch sight of him through the steam and say "Who the fuck's that?"

It's one of my great regrets that they never knew who their fathers were. I promised them that if I ever found out they'd be the second to know, after I told the CSA. It's a generational thing I suppose. I never knew who my dad was, and that same knowledge in turn has now been passed down to my kids.

The family unit, though, was what kept me going throughout the difficult years, and the kids have also been really supportive financially.

Trojan, my eldest, she did everything she could to try and bring in a bit of money, but you can only have one every nine months.

She's just had another beautiful little kid - Taser. That's the third she's had, from four different fathers. And one of them was twins. But it all helps to bring in a bit of income, which is what you need when you've got mouths to feed.

Trojan is much more settled now, but she was a wild one in her early days. I envy mothers who talk about how a photograph has perfectly captured their daughter. The last thing that perfectly captured my daughter was the military.

It all started innocently enough at nursery school when she got expelled for kidnapping one of the rich kids. I'm really surprised at the kid's parents though. Totally irresponsible. The ransom note clearly said 'No police, or Matthew dies,' but they still pressed charges. Total disregard for the welfare of the child.

It was tough for Troje, having a criminal record at the age of three.

To be fair though, Trojan did learn her lesson - she really knuckled down, and managed to keep totally out of trouble from then on until she was nearly four.

Then she fell out with her sister when our Troje gave the cat drugs, and it committed suicide. Well, it slipped off the roof, but cats don't tend to do that sort of thing unless they're totally off their heads, so once again Trojan got the blame.

Tange was very fond of that cat, especially when it was alive. But let's be honest, giving a cat drugs, we've all done it. It's just part and parcel of growing up and exploring your surroundings. Young minds are inquisitive. They're hungry to know things - the boiling point of a snail, how many breeze-blocks it takes to crush a tortoise, what happens when you pour candle wax into a sleeping adult's mouth - it's all just part of the learning process, and a kid's natural curiosity for its environment.

I always thought our Trojan would go on to be a scientist, or an explorer, or a dental hygienist. The ambition was there. But shyness held her back.

Nowadays they'd probably say she was borderline hamburgers, and she'd get a nice grant, but in those days, of course, we didn't have syndromes.

They've got one for every ailment now. You name it, they've got a syndrome for it.

Naughtiness - that's a syndrome now. Not learning to read properly, that's another. Swearing, not doing your homework, stealing, setting fire to somebody's house, boiling a snail - they're all syndromes now, whereas at one time it was just called being a vile kid. So in some ways I think Trojan was way ahead of her time.

Trouble always seemed to follow Trojan around. Like that time she took her driving test. It was a big day for her, so she'd had a few vodkas, just to steady her nerves, and then some pedestrian goes and walks right in front of her on the zebra - just never looked where he was going.

He's out of his coma now, so no harm done. But despite that, the driving instructor still failed her on two technicalities - insufficient use of the steering wheel, and failure to give a sample at the scene.

So then, of course, our Trojan had to resort back to driving illegally, which is what neither of us wanted. And that's how it is nowadays - you try and do the right thing, but the authorities just keep putting obstacles in your way, like pedestrians.

The one thing I most regret about Trojan, though, is that she never had my work ethic. She was always thinking of some 'get rich quick' scheme, which usually involved somebody else getting poor just as quick, rather than getting her head down, studying the forms, and putting in some serious time at the Job Centre claiming the benefits.

Okay, welfare may not be everybody's cup of tea, but it's a good, steady career if you're prepared to work at it.

But all's well that ends well. Trojan's fled the nest now and landed on her feet. She lives in a big posh place in London. Holloway Castle.

She still writes to me from time to time. She's got

her own letterhead with posh gates on it, and she's even got a job. She says she now works part-time in the library they've got down there, so that just shows you how important it was taking all them exams. I couldn't be more proud. Despite her underprivileged background, Trojan achieved five A-Levels, every one of them with a U* grade, and now she's ended up working in a library surrounded by books, so it can be done. Or was it the laundry? It was one of the two anyway.

Our Tangerine is nothing like her sister. Chalk and cheese. They probably take after their fathers. Tange was always happy to help out round the house. She was the one who'd go and fetch Doris to do the washing, or the ironing, or the hovering, or tell her there'd been a spillage.

Tange would also help out with a bit of retail work. And anybody who thinks that shoplifting's a soft option should try it. The police have even started clamping down on that now. I think the fine's gone up to two hundred and fifty pounds which, if you're caught, could wipe out a day's takings.

Have you noticed how they've also started putting them cardboard cut-outs of policemen in shops now? Crafty buggers. Well, our Tange, she got arrested by one of them. She got off in the end because he failed to read her her rights, but it was a nasty experience.

Don't get me wrong, I don't always condone theft, but what loving mother wouldn't be touched when her daughter steals her a foot spa for her birthday? It takes a special kind of dedication to get one of them things up your jacket.

I have to say, though, I only used it once, and then I put it in the car boot. In fact, I've spoken to a few people about this, and I'd love to know if there's anybody out there who's ever used a foot spa twice. Not that I'm ungrateful. I don't suppose that I'm the easiest woman to buy presents for. Our Trojan once got me a bread-maker. Let's face it, that was never going to happen. And one Christmas a few years back they all chipped in and got me an exercise DVD by that Carol Vaudeville. Not my cup of tea.

Having said that, I do enjoy a bit of exercise. When we first had the cat I saw it as an excuse to get fit, so I treated myself to one of them disability scooters so I could get into the habit of taking it for a walk every day. But the animal soon lost interest. It took to jumping on the scooter, which defeated the object of taking it for a walk. That cat was never quite the same after it committed suicide. We all get these health kick fads, but they don't last.

Tange is on a gap year now. She's been on a gap year for about three years. But she always wanted to do some travelling, so I did what any normal, caring mother would do. I got her a bus pass, and she went off on a mission.

She's got a bee in her bonnet - she wants to find her father and tap him up for a few quid. I said good luck with that.

So that just left me with my youngest, Trollop.

Now, our Troll's a good kid, but she's had a few problems with the authorities over the years. And I think that out of all of them she's the one who really did miss having a father-figure. Mind you, she was far too young to remember him. In fact, I don't think I can remember him. But if he's the one I think he was, he was a twat.

Anyway, to cut a long story short, after the incident with the old lady and the firework, they was going to put our Troll into care, so I applied to foster her.

It made perfect sense to me. After all, I already knew her, and she knew me, so there's no upheaval for the child. Troll gets to stay with her natural mother. Everybody's happy. And at four hundred and fifty quid a week, it seemed like a no-brainer.

But the authorities, of course, don't see it like that. It seems they'd rather give the money to a complete stranger, which seems ludicrous to me. Not that they could ever find anybody to take her on.

Troll can be pretty headstrong sometimes. I know how to deal with her, but she has been known to put people in hospital. Not that she'd ever lay a finger on me. Good as gold in that regard. With me it's just the verbal abuse. But Doris reckons they're all the same at that age.

"Sticks and stones, Doreen," she says. "We was all teenagers once."

I'm not sure Doris was, though. I reckon she was born aged about forty-five, she just seems to have such a sensible head on her. I've never seen Doris lose her temper, well, except the time she punched that politician in the throat at the Town Hall. But you know, we've all done that. And he was a lying prat so he had it coming.

When kids get into trouble, a lot of folks are quick to blame the parents. But a lot of folks don't have Troll as a kid. I've done my best to discipline Troll over the years. For instance, if she ever got into any trouble with the police, which has been known to happen, I made a point of nicking some money out of her purse.

You have to hit them where it hurts. Ironic that, actually, because the last time she got into trouble with the police it was because she'd hit somebody where it hurts. Another policeman. Well, that cost her thirty quid from me, on top of the court ruling, so she'll think twice before doing it again.

Troll was quite pleased when she finally managed to get herself a police record - the most amount of Anti-Social Behaviour Orders by one person in one street in any single year. She even asked about getting herself into The Guinness Book of Police Records, but they said it didn't count because it was wind-assisted. She did get one prestigious award, though, back in 2012. Despite some stiff competition from Dudley, our Troll was unanimously voted the 'West Midlands Young Offender of the Year' by the Neighourhood Watch, in partnership with the local Community Police.

She got a book token and a certificate, and she went on to represent the region in the finals, but lost to some chap from Manchester who kept setting fire to children's hospitals.

So yes, I'm proud of my kids, even though I wish I'd never had them.

They've all, in their own way, made their mark on the world against the odds. And nobody was more disappointed than me when they finally took Troll off to that remedial place. It was a desperate shame because, of all the kids, our Troll was the one that seemed to have the most about her - a genuine head for business and a bright future.

Okay, drug-dealing may not be the ideal career for a young lady, but she had ambitions to work her way up the step-ladder to become a proper drug's baron. And I bet you can't name me a poor drug's baron. Yes, she had real ambition, that one.

So that's a brief word about the neighbours and the kids.

But there's one more member of the family you still need to meet, and as it turned out she was the most important one of all.

CHAPTER SIX

OUR MIRIAM

Our Miriam is my auntie's mother's cousin's sister's nephew's daughter.

I'm the only family she's got left now, and she always comes round on a Thursday just for a bit of company. She's as old as a conker tree, and as deaf as a teenager that's been told to tidy her room.

The deafness can be a bit annoying. Miriam has got some hearing aids from the NHS, but I don't think they're the latest model, because they're attached to a headset made of Meccano, and powered by a 12 volt car battery built into her wheelchair. I think they were constructed in Russia just after the war. None of that matters though because she doesn't like to switch them on. I think they set fire to her ears once.

I've taken to communicating with Miriam using a megaphone that I bought from the car boot sale. It works pretty well, so I make Miriam pay for the batteries, which is only fair.

Our Miriam was born just after the First World War, and things were a lot different back then, she keeps telling me. There were no mobile phones, she says. And no phones that weren't mobile. No inside toilets, hardly any outside toilets, no electricity, gas, supermarkets, scratchcards, buses or computers, no Jeremy Kyle - or if there was he would have been in black and white. From the age of about eight years old, our Miriam used to have to get up at six in the morning, feed and bathe her mother and father, who were both disabled in the war, walk seven miles to school where they'd hit her with a stick, get back, milk the goats, cut down a tree, build a fire with no matches, strangle a chicken, boil some water, feed the family and the old woman next-door, plough the infertile soil in the allotment, darn some socks and then work on re-roofing the house by candlelight until she finally dropped off. And she calls them the good old days. From what Miriam tells me, I don't feel the wartime years would have been right for me. If I'd have lived back then I would definitely have opted to be one of them unconscious objectors.

Miriam's an authentic old Black Country lady, one

of the last of a generation that speaks in a dialect that even I struggle to fathom sometimes. Like all old deaf Black Country people, she speaks louder than a factory klaxon. No matter how bad her hearing, I'm sure she never has any trouble hearing herself. Her favourite word is "Eh??" which you'll hear about a hundred times when she visits. But she often uses other words that would puzzle many folk. If you don't know what a bobhowler is, or a fode, or a cogwinder, or gammitin, or tranklements, it can turn into a long afternoon. If you'm not from round here, I'll save you the trouble of looking them up.

A bobhowler is a large moth, a fode is the back yard, a cogwinder is a good punch, gammitin means playfully fighting or messing about, and your tranklements are your bits and pieces, your toys or possessions.

Our Miriam had no trouble using all five of them in one sentence. "They was a-gammitin on the fode with some tranklements and a big bobhowler londed on his yed so he gid it a right bloody cogwinder..."

Anyway, Miriam comes round every Thursday for a cup of tea and piece of cake. She's very cakey, our Miriam. Obviously, I have to get Doris in to help with the catering, otherwise it would get a bit much. Constantly boiling kettles, carrying cups and cutting cakes wouldn't suit my wrist. It's never been right since I had to fill in a form at the Job Centre. It's the same with opening tins, or stuff in packets.

As I've said before, I really don't know what I'd do without Doris. I'm sure she's got her own tins to open, but I suppose she has got Jack, and his power tools. It's different when you've got a handyman about the house.

Miriam especially likes fruitcakes. In fact, Doris reckons that Miriam is a fruitcake. Mind you, when Doris was slicing the cake one day she noticed the sell-by date was about a decade out. That's that bloody corner shop for you. That was the second thing I've had from there in the last few weeks that's been no good. I bought some frozen stuff from there the other day and then it comes on the telly that there was hoss-meat in it. I know there's a lot of it about, but you don't expect it in your fish-fingers do you? And I'm sure I found a bit of the saddle. They reckon it was a foreign factory that did it. Wales, I think.

Miriam still ate the cake, though.

"It should be all right," Doris said. "Fruit cakes last ages. They'm like wedding cakes. They usually last longer than the marriages."

Now, you may be wondering why I've devoted a whole chapter to our Miriam, who's basically an annoying deaf old bat in a wheelchair. Well, partly because she's family, and I won't hear a word said against her, but mainly because her part in my story turns out to be a big one.

You see, I didn't know it at the time, but all the hours I spent keeping her company would eventually pay dividends.

But more of that later.

First, let's put the country to rights.

PART TWO

THE STATE OF THE NATION

CHAPTER SEVEN
THE COST OF LIVING CRISIS

I don't really follow politics, but I do like to keep my eyes and ears open, at least while I'm awake, and me and Doris usually end up putting the world to rights when she pops round.

We reckon that them in Government are on another planet. The trouble is, politicians just aren't in touch with ordinary working folk, any more than I am. I mean, they talk about the cost of living crisis, but then in the next breath they say they're going to cut how much my benefits are going up by.

I bet the average politician couldn't tell you how much a loaf of bread was. Even Doris knows that. And I don't think that they realize just how much somebody like me, on benefits, needs just to keep up with rising inflammation.

Take food for example. A six-pack of cider has just gone up again, so I don't know how they expect any of us to have our five-a-day. And it's not even good enough these days just to have your proper portions. Now we're being told that we should only buy orgasmic products, even though they're often twice the price.

The Government won't admit it, but living in poverty makes it impossible to have a healthy diet. I learned how not to cook from my mother, who never had green fingers. Not surprisingly then, most busy working-class families turn to ready meals. But it's a big mistake. How can they call them ready meals when they need so much preparation before you can eat one? You're still expected to pull off cardboard outers, to puncture lids, push microwave buttons, stir it, microwave it again, rip off the plastic, and then provide your own plates and cutlery. By the time you've done all that you might as well have ordered from the takeaway. Don't get me wrong, I never chose to be this reliant on crisps. I'd much rather eat something better, but it isn't going to happen until they bring down the price of Pringles.

Meanwhile, my heating bills are going through the roof, literally. I mean, I had them solar plexus panels fitted on my roof, through some sort of grant, and what happens? It rained for three months solid. They went rusty and dropped off.

Troll was planning to use the panels to provide free heat to grow some cannabis in the loft. A whole crop had to go in the bin. Once again she shows a bit of enterprise and gets knocked back.

It's just one thing after another. The Winter Fuel Allowance is supposed to help with the heating bills. I put in for that and got turned down. Why? Because they discriminated against me on the grounds of age.

Not only is that illegal, it also doesn't make any sense. Pensioners aren't the only ones that get cold. In fact, old folks are probably warmer than the rest of us - they've got more bloody jumpers.

Some say that the welfare system just isn't fair, and they're right, because the whole thing is twisted in favour of them that have got jobs. Look at working tax credit, for example. It's an insult to anybody on benefits. Working people shouldn't get any benefits. They're working. They should be able to look after themselves, instead of spongeing off the likes of us.

And look at all the other perks they get. Wages. Holidays. Weekends off. And bonuses. I've been a loyal benefits claimant now for over twenty years, and I've never once been offered a bonus. It's just not a level playground. They're even trying now to cut back on my disability allowance, just because I'm not technically disabled. Well, maybe not in their eyes, but they only see what they want to see. It's a disgrace. We all know that arms and legs only respond to signals from the brain, and if mine don't get any, what am I supposed to do?

I tell you now, the Government have got to sort it out quick, or there'll be more riots.

And talking of riots, I do fear for my kids. They went down to London in 2011, to do their bit, you know, to help out with the protests. They came back with two pairs of trainers. Hardly covered the bloody train fare - not that they had tickets. It's no wonder that the youngsters today turn to drug-dealing.

I mean, what prospects have they got?

Take our Troll, she's been out of school for over a year now. Well, a bit longer than that if you count the truancy. And what chance has she got of finding a job?

You hear horror stories of, like, a hundred people applying for one job. There was one in the free paper recently, a nice little job, working in a florist. Now that would have been perfect for our Troll, because she likes shops. So what happened?

Two hundred and sixty-three people applied for the

same job. She had no chance. Or to be more precise, she only had a one in two hundred and sixty-three chance of getting it. Well, actually no, worse than that, because she wasn't one of the ones that applied.

Anyway, I told her to get up that Job Centre. It's about time she started to pull her weight and earned an honest day's benefits.

But our Troll wasn't interested. Head in the clouds. Face buried in her mobile all day long, playing about with unsociable media. And now she's ended up getting a job in that remedial place as an in-mate. It strikes me that the kids of today just think the world owes them a living, that they can sit on their arses and the money will just come in by itself. I didn't fight a world war for that to happen. In fact, I didn't fight a world war at all, and it's still happened. So yes, if you ask me the country's going to the dogs.

But that's today's bloody politicians for you. Too busy fiddling their expenses and sipping champagne at gay weddings to sort the country out.

It's all right for them, sat up there in their ivory Tardis. They want to try living in the real world, like me, like the ordinary woman in the street, or on the sofa. They want to try bringing up my daughters. They wouldn't be so bloody smug then.

There was a Partly Political Broadcast on the telly

the other night, and all they kept going on about was hard-working families.

But what about the rest of us?

It's a good job some of us have got the gumption to get off our backsides and claim the welfare, because I tell you now, nobody else will do it for you. The fact is, a politician wouldn't have the first clue what it's like trying to live off the state.

And that's another thing - that expenses scandal. They've all got two houses each, whereas I've got to make do with one, and they've only got to have a shit and they're claiming extra money for the toilet paper. But with me, and millions like me, we know that every penny we spend has to come out of our weekly allowance. So, every single day, people on welfare are faced with some really tough choices. Five extra scratchcards might mean cutting back on the orgasmic fruit and veg, or the kids' toothpaste. It could even mean the difference between buying a new pair of trainers, and stealing them.

These are the sort of decisions no self-respectable mother should have to face in modern-day twentieth century Britain.

It also seems that the politicians don't even try to put the proper incentives in place for ordinary folk to better themselves. If you ask me, they like us just where we are - under the thumbnail. I mean, take a classic example. The Government always claim that they want more entrepioneers, but when Doris's husband Jack applied to the bank for a loan for his plumbing business, what happened? They said he had to put up his house as cholesterol.

Jack told them where they could stick it. Well, he didn't quite put it like that, obviously. He just told them to fuck off. He couldn't have put up the house for cholesterol anyway, as it happens, because it's rented. But the principle remains the same. The fact is, the Government, the ruling classes, don't want us working classes getting above our station.

And don't even get me started on the bankers. You can't tell me it's a coincidence that the word rhymes with…well, I won't say it, in case there's any kids reading this, but as far as I'm concerned they can all fuck off where they came from. We worked it out once. A typical banker's annual bonus would keep the likes of me and Doris going for over a month. It's a scandal.

How can anybody be worth over a million pounds just for sitting in a bank? That's more than a decent scratchcard win, and I have to gamble hard-earned money to win that. And you have to scratch the foil off properly, which isn't always as easy as it looks.

Bankers, politicians, the police, the Job Centre bloke, they're all in it together if you ask me.

Apart from that lot of fat cats though, it's hard for everybody at the minute. I mean the Government have said that we'll probably be on these hostility measures for years yet, and there's no sign of any light at the end of the funnel. So, unless you're a banker, or a politician, or a professional footballer playing for Chelsea, or you work at the Job Centre, what hope have you got?

The Leader of the Inquisition came on the telly the other day, and he kept wittering on about the cost of living crisis. But he conveniently forgot to mention that he was a multi-billionaire. Well, they all am. It said on the news that they all own private moats, and I bet they don't come cheap. Doris bought a hot-tub, and that was hundreds, so God knows what a moat would cost - especially a heated one.

But at the other end of the sphinctum, you get the likes of me, who can't even afford a decent holiday.

There was a time when I'd try to fit in three or four holidays a year, because we all need our rest. But just lately that's been impossible. For a start, it's not easy getting time off from the Job Centre these days. They want me to go every week now, so I think they must be short-staffed.

Then there's the cost. An all-inclusive luxury break somewhere hot is thousands, and there don't seem to be the grants available that there used to be. Once again they seem to expect me to fork out from my own pocket.

But of course, it's not just me it affects. Doris was worried about leaving me without any house-help, which is understandable, so this year I had to go on holiday with her and Jack. Ten days in Barmouth at their caravan. Not that I'm ungrateful, but it was a bloody nightmare, for three main reasons.

For a start, it took three of the ten days to get there, as Jack's such a steady driver. Jack's the only driver I know that, when the road's at a standstill, it doesn't slow him down. As it happened, the M5 seized up at Michaelwood services, just after junction 13, so we decided to stop for a wee, and to give Doris a chance to stretch my legs. We shouldn't have bothered. The queue for the toilets went back to junction 8. And by the time we finally got back in the car Jack needed a shave. Luckily, I find it fairly easy to sleep on long journeys, as well as on short journeys. I normally have a bit of a nap in the taxi on the way to the Job Centre on a Wednesday. It's only ten minutes there and back, but it freshens me up and keeps me alert in case they ask any crafty questions. I felt a bit sorry for Jack though, because it must be harder to have a decent sleep when you're driving. Though to be honest, at the speed he goes, I don't think he'd do much damage if he did.

The second reason it was a nightmare is because we stopped in a caravan.

How anybody can think it's relaxing to spend time in a tin box is beyond me. Doris and Jack have had this one for about twenty years, and it wasn't built with comfort in mind. When we first arrived at the site, I thought it was just the portaloo, so I was a bit surprised when Jack unlocked it and took my case in. It was quite late, and it took him about an hour messing about outside and swearing in a cupboard before he got some lights on. Only then could I see the full extent of the horror. The telly was miniature, with a bent paper clip for an aerial, and you could only get Welsh programmes on it. You can't tell me that's a real language. It just sounds like somebody's trying to spit at you.

It took another three-quarters of an hour to boil the kettle, and the only milk Jack could get from the camp shop was that VHS stuff in a cardboard box. It tasted like urine, and I should know.

There was no Sky dish, no bath, no central heating, the fridge made a noise like a mosquito, and the mattress was so soft I had to be air-lifted to hospital on the second morning, and spent the rest of the week in a girdle.

The third reason it was a nightmare - it was Wales.

It stopped raining once, at about half-past two on the Thursday morning, for twelve minutes. I know this for a fact because when it rains on a tin box, it's loud. I don't think I ever got more than nine hours sleep any night, so I was waking up shattered.

Now, I don't know if you've ever spent ten days in a caravan with Doris and Jack in Wales - probably not - but when there's no plasma and it's raining non-stop the minutes don't exactly fly by. You find yourself opening corner cupboards to see what's in them, and then looking through leaflets advertising tourist attractions for the whole family.

I'm not usually an avid reader, but I did read all the leaflets about eight times, because there was nothing else to do. There was 'Paperweight World: a unique collection of paperweights of historical significance, including some from the roaring twenties.' I didn't really fancy that.

Then there was 'Wasp World: a unique collection of wasps, which you can observe in their natural habitat without getting stung.' There was a faded picture of a child with pig-tails looking amazed and pointing with the mom and dad behind her, grinning.

They were stood one side of some glass, and on the other side there were some bins, with wasps and a rotting apple. And it was a tenner each to get in, so in a way you did get stung. Actually, it's probably a lot more than a tenner, as the date on the leaflet was 1981.

Our nearest tourist attraction, about an hour by car, or three hours if Jack's driving, was a corrugated metal shed with a lamb inside. Lamb World, it was called. You queued up for forty minutes to touch it on the head. Thirty-five quid to get in, seven pound fifty for an ice cream. The kids got a free sticker, but we didn't have any kids, and they wouldn't offer us a discount.

I didn't want to sound ungrateful in front of Jack, because he'd paid for me as well, but I'd rather have stayed at home, and I told him so to his face.

We had to cut the holiday short in the end. Another three days to get home. All in all, it wasn't exactly a fortnight in Barbados, like I was used to when I first went on the welfare. And frankly it's no holiday for Doris either when she's got to take all my ironing.

So anyway, the long and short of it is, this cost of living crisis is affecting not just me, but the people who work for me. And on top of all that lot, we're expected to provide for ourselves when we retire.

There was a budget a few weeks back, and the Chancellor of the Expressor was going on and on about pension pots. Well, where's my pension pot? I've only got one pot. It's upstairs under the bed, and it hasn't got a bloody pension in it, I can tell you.

So, I can't see myself retiring any time soon. And we all know what's going to happen then, don't we.

Thanks to the short-sighted politicians, people like me are going to end up having to live off the state forever.

And it'll serve the buggers right.

CHAPTER EIGHT

EDUCATION, EDUCATION, EDUCATION.

I once applied to be a teacher.

Now, I've got nothing against teachers, as people. But as teachers, well…

They start work at nine, and they finish at three, so that's what…two hours. Then they have about six months off in the Summer, a month at Easter, two months at Christmas, half-term, full-term, Whitsun, bank holidays, teacher-training days, a fortnight off when it snows, and then they retire at thirty on a full pension and come back the next day part-time on twice the money. No wonder the kids nowadays are struggling.

A few years ago they made me go to one of them parent's evenings, because they said our Tange was one of the ones that was struggling a bit. She'd come bottom of the class, apparently, out of thirty. Well, that's not bad is it?

I mean, when I went to school I came bottom out of forty-five. And that's the thing - if they'd only keep the class sizes a bit smaller, our Tange might have come bottom out of, like, nine or something. But they don't see it like that. They just won't put the resources in.

The head teacher even agreed with me that smaller class sizes would be a good thing. So Tange tries to help, by not turning up, and then she gets put in detention. There's no sense in it.

They ran a pilot scheme at our local school last year, where they had fourteen teachers to each pupil, and it was really successful. Re-offending rates were down marginally, exam results were up two percent, and teachers found they could take extra holidays in term-time, so it was a win-win. I'll never understand why the Government didn't roll it out nationally.

Where I admit our Tange did struggle, though, was on the discipline side.

The school week started, they reckoned, at 9am on a Monday. Well, our Tange normally liked to put in an appearance at about 2pm, on a Wednesday - a bit like me with the Job Centre.

So of course they had a go at me about that, like it was my fault. But what was I supposed to do? She wouldn't get out of bed, and there was no way I was getting up at that time to wake her.

The school also operated a zero-tolerance policy on drugs. Three misdemeanours in any one week and the kid gets a written warning to take to the parents. Three written warnings and you get a sticker. At one point they even barred Tange from a maths lesson, so as you can imagine, she was gutted.

Three stickers, and the school gets the local police involved, who I think have their own sticker system, particularly if the child's been dealing. So as you can see, they don't stand for any nonsense.

Don't get me wrong, I think education is a really important part of a person's education. In fact I even thought about going to college recently, to improve myself. I found a nice little course at the local Polytechnical in Walsall - Pottery & Human Rights. It was free for the unwaged and I thought it sounded quite interesting. And it's not the sort of thing that employers are looking for, so it was perfect for me. But in the end I couldn't get the student loan.

Looking back, I definitely feel that I missed out when I was younger, so like any responsible mother I insisted that my kids went to school occasionally.

But some of the stuff they teach now, what use is it? They said that one of the subjects our Tange was struggling with was, you know, the Shakespeare. But she's never been interested in anything foreign, so unless Tange is intending to go and live abroad, when's she ever going to need that? She did come home one day and told me that they was studying Omelette. But I thought it was a cooking class, not some bloody Shakespearian story book.

Anyway, after a few false starts and a couple of minor arson incidents, neither of which was ever totally proven, our Tangerine knuckled down. And I'm really proud of her, because in the end she was the first of our generation of Tiptons to be awarded Special Educational Needs.

She got all her qualifications. She got her ADHD with Honours (that's both her inattentive, and her hyperactive-impulsive) and she also achieved all her other syndromes, her hamburgers, and her dyslexia.

On the strength of that, the local authority got all the extra funding. But of course it didn't come to the family that earned it - no, it went to the school. The system's all wrong.

So anyway, I didn't get the teacher's job. They just don't like it when you speak your mind.

In the summer, having successfully completed her

secondary education, Tangerine and I sat down to discuss her future. Well, I was already sitting down. Like most kids these days, she really wanted to go to Uni. You can get thousands now on a student loan, and you don't have to pay it back until you get a job, so, like...never. But it was the thought of all that studying - it put Tange off. Even the media studies course she found, which analyzed the social impacts of watching the Jeremy Kyle show all day, seemed to involve some reading.

So in the end she applied to see if she could get the loan without doing the course, but there was too much red tape and it fell through. Tange knows lots of students who've done that - got the money but not turned up for the lessons. But she got turned down, and she was gutted. I told her, she should have just said to them that she was going to turn up and then not bothered, rather than getting penalized for telling the truth. It really annoys me that some people just know how to work the system.

Tange has given up on education now, and set her sights on being a teacher. Apparently, it's just like being a student, but you get paid as well.

Of course, in my day, the Universities were just for the privileged few, not for the working classes. Not that I ever worked, as such, but I always saw myself as working-class, and things were very different for us. In my day, you left school, walked straight onto the dole queue, and that was your job for life. Some ended up as factory-fodder, but the smarter and more ambitious ones went on the welfare.

Now, nearly every kid wants to just go to Uni, snort drugs and walk out with a fifty grand debt. But what sort of future is that for youngsters? I mean, if they could actually have the fifty grand to spend on the drugs, that might at least give them a better start in life. And even if it didn't, they wouldn't notice.

Yes, you can say what you like about having no education and being on welfare, but I've never owed anybody a penny. It's always been the other way around.

And that's something they don't teach you at Uni.

CHAPTER NINE

FOREIGNERS

Everybody's too scared to say it, but you have to blame the foreigners.

Of course, you can't say that these days. No, you've only got to mention foreigners and you're accused of being a rapist. Now don't get me wrong. I know this is the 20th century, and we all live in a diverted and multifunctional society. And I think it's great that we've got the Indian restaurant down the road. And the Chinese. And I mean, you can't expect them to commute can you?

But let's face it, it's gone too far now.

I mean, I was born here - I belong here. But it's got to the stage now where some of the people who don't belong here were actually born here. So there's no way they're going to want to go home now is there? They probably wouldn't even remember what home looks like.

And if you ask me, half of them are terrorists. Well, more than half. There's one down the road here in Cannock. They reckon he's plotting to blow up the chip shop.

And the thing is, now that we're all in the EU, the Government can't do anything about it. I mean take that clerical radish - what's his name? The one with the beard, and the hook...Abu Gadaffi. Well, the Government tried to export him, didn't they? They told him to sling his hook. And what happened? He was just loffin at us. Bloody loffin at us, he was. In fact, the UK has become the loffinstock of Europe. It's because we're ruled by Brussels. They come over here, they take all your jobs, and that's when they become a drain on society.

I mean, take an example. What hope did my Trojan have of getting that job as a doctor, up against that Indian bloke with that medical degree? She had no chance did she?

It's pure prejudice. They just took one look at her qualifications, and that was it. As I've already said, I don't really follow politics, but it strikes me that this country does some stupid things. One of the things we seem really good at is collecting money from our hard-working citizens, and then sending it all over the world. Don't get me wrong, I don't mind helping out with the odd earthquake, or some other disaster involving foreigners, especially if it wasn't their fault. In fact, I often get Doris to text in some money from her mobile if something on the telly touches me. I think she bought a mosquito net last week, but it hasn't arrived yet. But sending millions from Government to help terrorists build rockets seems a bit daft to me. The general rule of thumb seems to be, the more a country hates us, the more money we send them.

Talking of which, apparently even half the Scottish folk want to be foreigners now.

They had a vote about it recently, and England lost.

I don't know much about the Scots, other than they wear kilts and they're mean, but Doris reckons that they get a lot more welfare money than we do. She looked into the idea of me emigrating there once, but it's too bloody cold, and Doris said it would be too far for her to come to do the ironing, so we gave up on it. But one thing's for sure, if the Scots are getting extra welfare, it will be the likes of me that's subsidizing that. So that's another reason not to trust foreigners. Oh, yes, and they eat porridge.

And then there's the likes of Jack next-door, and his plague of Polish plumbers. It used to be the case that Jack could turn up for a burst pipe job whenever he liked, weeks after the emergency call, and get the thing sorted in his own way. But now, if he so much as delays by a day or two, he finds a Polish plumber has nipped in and stolen the work. Not only that, they've charged half what Jack would have done. It's just not the British way.

Okay, I suppose that some of you might argue that technically Jack's an immigrant as well, being a Brummie by birth, but he's been accepted into the community now, he's learnt the language, and feels almost like one of us.

It's a good job Jack's still got a contract with the local school to keep an eye on their pipes, otherwise he'd be suffering. Doris says he's freelance now, so if he doesn't work, he doesn't earn.

He used to work for the gas board, but they laid him off in the last recession, following some sort of cock-up with a leaking valve joint and a crafty fag. The headquarters needed refurbishing anyway, Jack said, so he did them a bit of a favour. Not that they deserved it, after the way they treated him.

The only way Jack's been able to keep his earnings stable since is to charge his full week's money to whichever job he manages to do in that period. It's sometimes a bit harsh on old ladies who might only need a tap washer changing - they get a bill for four hundred quid if Jack's done nothing else that week - but if they ever complain Jack tells them to take it up with the Polish.

Most of the old folk remember the war, even the ones who are a bit demented, so that tends to shut them up.

Just lately though, I can see how the stress of work is really affecting Jack.

I just hope that never happens to me.

CHAPTER TEN

THE BEST OF BRITISH

Even though it may seem to some that I'm always moaning about this country, I'd be the first to recognize that Britain does have some things that are considered to be the envoy of the world.

The monarchy, the BBC, the NHS, the prisons and even the welfare system - these are all great British prostitutions which we should treasure. Yes, they do have their faults, but it's nothing that injections of unlimited amounts of cash wouldn't cure.

Take the monarchy, for example. Everyone agrees that the Queen is a fantastic role model - a brilliant example of how an ordinary woman can provide for a growing family and successfully live off the state. But even they've had to suffer cut-backs to make ends meet. The man who puts the toothpaste on the brush for Charles has apparently had to double-up on jobs and now looks after the toilet paper as well. And the corgis are down to six sachets a day and the occasional dead pheasant.

Okay, I know the Royals do get some privileges. Free foreign holidays (Philip in particular seemed to like to taunt the foreigners, which always gets my vote) free tickets to the Olympics, Commonwealth Games, and all the other Paul McCartney and Gary Barlow concerts. The Queen also has two birthdays, so she can double-up on presents, so I bet she's got at least a couple of foot spas - one for each royal foot, looked after by a footman. And I notice that Royals seem to get doctor's appointments quicker than I can. But I also know that despite all that they're still finding things tough. I read somewhere that they were even having to sell off some of the royal works of art. One portrait in particular of the Queen by Rolf Harris was recently going cheap on eBay. They surely wouldn't get rid of that unless they really needed the money.

The second of our great British constitutions is the BBC. Now, I must admit, the BBC is a bit of a sore point for me. The television licence is the only time I ever pay tax, so it rather spoils my record. I asked my ghost-writer to do some research, and it turns out that the BBC collects over five billion pounds a year from people with televisions, and also from quite a few people who don't, but are too scared to ignore the letters. From what I can see, they give most of the money to David Walliams and Miranda, and a big chunk of the rest goes on taking thousands of their staff to five-star hotels abroad to watch the world cup. It may surprise some of you, but I'm not a natural sports lover. I enjoy the odd game of bingo, but not if it starts getting competitive.

Then, with what's left of our taxpayers' money, the BBC makes a couple of telly programmes designed to entertain the masses. The trouble is, about 99% of them are cooking programmes. I did a quick check recently on the BBC and counted nearly six hundred cooking programmes in one week. I might have missed one or two. But to be honest I can't be doing with any of them.

What's that expression about too many cooks? As I said before, I'm not a keen cook myself, so watching somebody else bake a cake is not really my idea of entertainment. I'd rather touch a lamb on the head.

So that just leaves me with East Bloody Enders. Lots of angry cockney folk shouting at each other. That's no way to relax after a hard day.

Oh, yes, and I've just remembered that other thing

the BBC does that I can't watch. Celebrities in Need. Lots of crap actors desperately trying to stay famous, bleating on about sending money to somebody else somewhere or other. They give up ten minutes of their time to swim a width of the local baths to raise awareness of their career and then expect us to drop everything and send them loads of money. Why don't they just send it themselves? They've got a damn sight more of it than I have. Even some really famous actors feel that they have to visit Africa once a year, hold a kid and cry a lot on camera, otherwise their celebrity status might die. Just shut your traps and give them the money yourself I say. No need to go on telly.

Now, if that sounds like I'm bitter, think about this. The thing is, I can watch Jeremy Kyle for nothing, but of course I still have to fork out for the licence, even though I don't like angry cockney folk, sport, cooking, Miranda, David Walliams, more cooking, celebrities in need and yet more cooking, so that doesn't strike me as fair. Some people say the BBC occasionally makes a drama that looks a million dollars, but that isn't very hard if you've spent two million dollars doing it. And to be honest I'm not a great fan of them period pain dramas either - lots of women sitting around sewing, and surly blokes in leather boots riding horses and smoking cigars.

In short, the BBC might be worthy of being called a great British destitution, but I'd like to see it be a little bit more careful about what it does with my hard-earned cash.

Better still, it should be free. Personally I'd rather watch adverts than the BBC programmes, and a decent advert break gives Doris the chance to make me a cup of tea. And on top of all that - in fact on top of the house - I've got a Sky dish. I don't have to pay for that, so why should I have to pay for the ordinary aerial?

Our Tangerine organized the Sky dish a few years back. I'm not sure how it all works, because I think normally you're supposed to pay some sort of monthly prescription, but the bloke up the car boot wired it all up for her and no money changed hands. I think she might have swapped it for a foot spa.

There's no way I was paying Sky a monthly fee for a signal they was beaming out anyway. It's no skin off their nose how many people look at it, is it? In fact, they should be glad of the extra ratings. It's a bit like buses. They should let you get on for free if they're going that way anyway. It's the same with the internet. What's the point of paying for another wireless connection when the house next door has already got one? It doesn't cost Doris any extra to share it with me, so it's a win-win.

So that brings us on to the NHS. Where do I start?

As you've already heard, I've had a few run-ins with the NHS over the years. Once again, I got my ghost-hunter to do some research, and apparently the NHS is the country's biggest employer. Nearly one and a half million people work for it, but the trouble is only about twelve of them are doctors. The rest tend to be pen-pushers, the ones that write you a letter saying how long you've got to wait to see one of the twelve doctors. So that needs sorting for a start. They also employ too many of them plastic sturgeons. I'm sorry, but having a big nose is not a life-threatening illness. If it was I'm sure our Miriam wouldn't have made it to ninety. Her nose is like the Concorde, but I wouldn't expect tax-payers' money to put it right.

Where does it end? Ugly people being cured? Fat people being cut down to size? If you ask me, the only operation the NHS should do on fat people is sewing their mouths up.

And then there's that latest scandal, them gay and trans-thespian women being injected with sperm. What's that all about? They need to think that through a bit. You can't have a sperm bank without there being some sort of sperm bankers, wanting more bonuses and pensions. Ordinary bankers are bad enough. But can you just imagine what sort of wankers sperm bankers would be? And then there's all sorts of ethical questions to be answered. What happens if somebody robs a sperm bank? Is it theft or kidnapping?

I think the NHS is just taking on far too much. And meanwhile I can't even get an appointment for the backlash on my neck unless I'm prepared to buy one of next year's diaries.

I told you before how it took four years to get me fast-tracked to the hospital. By the time I got there I'd forgotten why I was going, so they put me at the back of the queue again.

I suppose the NHS is a bit like the BBC, and all them other companies in the pubic sector - too much free money, too many pen-pushers, too much waste. A woman up the bingo who works for them told me how it operates. When I run out of tea-bags, I just ask Doris to nip to the corner shop and get some; when the NHS runs out of tea-bags the nurses have to tell a manager to fill in a form to order some from a special supply company, which delivers them eight weeks later. And because it's the NHS, they get them at a special price of fifteen pounds a bag.

If they'd just cut out the waste there'd be money to spend on more important things, like welfare. They could even afford an extra couple of doctors. But instead they prefer to pay for it all by charging people with sick relatives eighteen quid to park near the hospital for half an hour. I'm glad I haven't got a car. Or a sick relative.

But despite all that, the NHS is still admired all over the world. In fact, folk come from all over the world to try it out. Foreigners know they can fly in, get their operation, have a fifteen-quid cup of tea, and bugger off without paying. They even use taxis so they don't have to park. Some then decide to stop a bit longer than it said on the visa, and get given a job working for the NHS. And guess who's paying for it all? Well, not me, but I bet a few of you reading this might be.

One of Doris's nieces went to live in Australia, and she says they don't stand for any of that nonsense there. If you can't pay your way, they kick you out. That sounds like my sort of country. At one time I thought of denigrating there when I retire. It's hotter than Scotland, and our Troll wanted to go because she said it's the place they make Home And Away, which I didn't know, but I'm not sure how I stand on the welfare, because the rules are a bit different over there. And I don't suppose I could persuade Doris to come, or even to commute, which would leave me in the lurch a bit.

Anyway, Australia brings me nicely onto convicts,

and the prison system. Unlike the other topics, this is something I do feel strongly about.

We're in urgent need of penile reform in this country. As you know, my daughters have had one or two brushes with the law over the years, and reading between the lines I reckon they've spent some time inside. Not that they'd ever let on, of course - they're good girls and they wouldn't want to worry me - but when your kids keep disappearing without a word for twelve months at a time, a mother's instinct kicks in.

We've always been a close family, so suspecting one of your children might be locked up somewhere is not a nice feeling. Personally I've never been behind bars, even in pubs, but I've seen enough on telly to know it's not a pleasant environment.

The drugs, the bullying, the violent threats, they wouldn't be a problem to somebody like our Trojan, in fact she'd probably excel at it, but I know she wouldn't like the games of chess, the Bible reading, the gym sessions, and all the other stuff I've seen bored inmates doing on telly. And she certainly wouldn't appreciate being locked up without a mobile phone. She'd see that as a punishment.

I did hear something the other day about the EU wanting to give our prisoners the vote. That's not something I agree with. I can see why they want to do it - the low turn-up figures for voting is terrible at the moment, even for the general erections, so it would help the politicians to get a few more votes. But there's probably enough people in prison now to overthrow the Government, so they have to be careful. If they all voted for a new party that stood for getting rid of prisons, they'd probably get in, and then all the prisoners would get out. Okay, that might help one or two of my daughters, but we'd also be letting out all the mass-murderers, the rapists and the pediatricians, so if I was the EU ministers I'd think that through a bit more carefully.

Obviously, prison does have its advantages. Three free meals a day cooked by your own chef; no rent, rates, insurance, gas or electricity bills to pay; no TV licence; a chance for further education without any student debt - the list goes on. But it doesn't really appeal to me. I can get most of that anyway from the comfort of my own home, and think I'd struggle if I didn't have Doris in the cell next door.

The last great British inscription on my list was the welfare system.

I've already expressed my views on this topic elsewhere in this book, so I don't want to go over old ground, but it needs saying that nowhere else in the world is there a system to match the British one, except possibly the Scottish one, but that doesn't count because they're basically just robbing from the British one. Yes, we all know it's not perfect, and yes, they could always do more to ease the burden of modern-day living for people like me - simple things like delivering scratchcards to the door, for example, would make a big difference. There are some days when I simply don't feel like getting up and going out. And sometimes Doris may be at the factory so I have to fend for myself.

For that matter, just giving Doris a proper carer's allowance wouldn't come amiss. She doesn't need the money herself because she's working, but she could pass it on to me, and it would at least cover a few of the basic necessities, like crisps, or perhaps even the occasional treat, like Pringles.

But having said all of that, I wouldn't swap the British welfare system for anything, except perhaps a good lottery win, or an even better welfare system. It kept me afloat when I needed it most, which was all the time, being a non-swimmer.

I know that some of you reading this, the country's working tax-payers, might be thinking "Yes Doreen, but I'm paying for that. How much have you cost me over the years?"

It's a fair question, but I think the answer might

surprise you, and make you see things differently.

Once again I got my ghost-rider to look into this and do some calculations. He estimated my entire welfare bill over the past twenty years, since the day I was first diagnosed with Lazy Cow Syndrome.

According to the official Government figures from HMRC, there were just over 29 million taxpayers in this country in 2014. So, there it is, in black and white. All I've cost you is just one pound each. Yes, one pound - the price of a scratchcard.

I'm sure you'll agree that's a bargain.

And as if you needed more proof that your money was well-spent, you're about to hear how this vital safety-net kept body and soul together during the most difficult time of my life - my darkest hours.

PART THREE

MY DARKEST HOURS

CHAPTER ELEVEN
ROCK BOTTOM

With our Trojan, Tangerine and Troll all gone, the house was a lot quieter, and I hit rock bottom.

I never thought I'd miss the kids, but until it stopped I didn't realize just how much I'd got used to the buzz of having people around, the banter, the rows, the screaming, the filthy language, the playful violence, the piles of unconscious bodies littered on the lounge floor, the police raids. I still had Doris, of course, and the visits of our Miriam on a Thursday, but it was never quite the same. My little magpies had fled the nest, and for the first time in my life I was feeling lonely.

I'm ashamed to admit it now, but I started drinking heavily. At one point, I was downing bottles of stout faster than Doris could get the tops off and pour them. In fact, it was Doris who suggested that I changed to brandy to cut down on the recycling.

Instead of falling asleep at half-past eight like I used to, I found I was passing out halfway through watching Jeremy Kyle in the afternoon. And instead of waking up, I was regaining consciousness.

At one point the priest came round, because Doris was so worried about me that she'd had a word, and he tried to comfort me. He said - and I'm sure he meant well - he said, "What you really need Doreen, is a good man to take you up the aisle." I'm not sure if he was putting himself forward for the job, but I said "No, Father. Not at my time of life."

When you get the wrong side of forty you tend not to be as stretchy as you once were, and at my age the thought of inviting a man back into my bed was too much to handle. If I'm honest, I've never enjoyed sex, and it wouldn't surprise me if the men I've been with didn't feel the same.

Don't get me wrong, I've had my moments. You don't end up with three kids without a few sticky encounters. But sex? At my time of life? No thank you, love. Much as I like a lie-down.

Maybe I've never done it right, I don't know, but the few times I've been on the receiving end of a man's attentions I've felt more like the victim of a burglary. Breaking and entering in the dead of night, that's all it was.

If you ask me, men are only after one thing, and I haven't got it. That's the main reason I never got married. Well, that and the fact that nobody ever offered to marry me.

It may surprise some of you to learn that I've never been very posthumous with men, but it's true. My problem is that, on the rare occasions I dropped my guard, such as when I was asleep, I always seemed to end up fertilized. Most burglars break in and take things - mine broke in and left something.

Trojan, Tangerine, Troll - they were all one-night stands. In fact, every relationship I've ever had has been a one-night stand. Men never seem to want to come back for a second go, and that's suited me just fine. Not that I wouldn't have tracked the blokes down if I could have. After all, a bit of maintenance money wouldn't have come amiss now and again. But the authorities wanted the sort of details I just wasn't in a position to give, such as their names, and a vague description.

So no, priest's advice or not, getting a man in was not an option.

I knew that if I was going to get out of this crisis, it

had to come from me; I had to do it myself. It's been that way all my life - I've never relied on the help of others, and I wasn't about to start now.

I asked Doris to get me some self-help books out of the library, and to read me a few extracts while she was ironing. We got into a little routine. She'd read me a chapter, then pour me a brandy, then another chapter, another brandy, and we'd carry on like that until I passed out and she tucked me in. Then, after a couple of weeks, she'd start reading me two chapters before pouring the brandy, another two chapters, and so on. Bit by bit, she was cutting down my drinking. In one way, binge-drinking did help me cut back on the amount I drank overall, because it increased the amount of time I was unconscious. Looking back at those few years now, I'd say they were definitely the low point of my life. Well, that's what Doris reckons anyway. I'm buggered if I can remember any of it. But she says it was far worse than when I was diagnosed with Lazy Cow; worse even than giving birth to my kids.

But they say that things are always darkest before it gets a bit lighter, and that's how it proved to be. I'm not quite sure how or why it happened, but one afternoon, I just woke up, and I realized I was fed up of reaching for the bottle.

So I moved the bottle a bit bloody nearer.

But you know that old expression 'One door closes and another one shuts'? Well, that happened to me. Just when I thought things couldn't possibly get any worse, I had a letter come through the post.

I'll never forget how my hand trembled when I got Doris to open that envelope, and how the beads of sweat dripped from my brow as she began to read it out loud.

My worst fear - the worst fear of any mother - had come true.

And I sobered up immediately.

CHAPTER TWELVE
THE JOB FROM HELL

I've never seen the smarmy Job Centre counsellor looking quite so smarmy.

"Well, as you know, it's good news, Mrs Tipton. We've found you a job."

It turned out that the shoe factory where Doris cleaned was very busy on the run-up to Christmas, and the packing machine had packed up. They were waiting for some parts to come from China, but in the meantime they were desperate for some casual labour. So desperate, in fact, that they were even willing to take me on, on a one month trial, without an interview. The smarmy counsellor had apparently phoned them and said, "If it's casual labour you want, Doreen's your woman. They don't come any more casual than her."

I pointed out how weak my wrist was, and that I was still suffering from backlash on the neck. I also pointed out that the factory was in walking distance, and I had trouble walking. I even pointed out that it had recently been my birthday, but he just didn't want to know.

"You're well aware of the rules, Mrs Tipton," he said with an evil grin. "If you don't take this job, we'll have to look at stopping your benefits."

That was on the Wednesday, and on the following Monday morning I was expected to be at the factory at half-past eight and report for duty, or they were going to cut me off without a penny.

First thing I did when I got home was phone the doctor, but I couldn't get an appointment until the Tuesday, as I'm not one of the Royal Family. Even The Citizens Advice Squad was on half-day closing. So then I tried phoning one of them 'no win, no fee' solicitors off the telly, but they were southerners and seemed to struggle understanding me.

I had a word with Doris to see if she could do my shift for me, but she was already doing a triple shift that day because two of her mates were ill, and then there was my housework to do.

It was a nightmare.

The bastards had got me cornered.

I couldn't risk losing the benefits, so in the end I decided to show up for a few minutes and then go all faint. I probably would naturally go all faint anyway, so it would all be above-board.

I went to bed a bit earlier that night, at five. I had to set the alarm for twenty-five past eight the next morning, because the factory was a good couple of minutes away on foot. Not that I was going on foot. I got Jack to give me a lift. It might have been quicker walking, as he's such a steady driver, but he got me there just in time, about ten minutes late.

The shoe factory is now the only industry left in the area, since Thatcher shut down the galvanized bucket furnace in the eighties. It's been there years, since I was a kid, and probably employs about 90% of the locals who've got a job. But 90% of the locals haven't got a job. And until today I was one of them.

I was surprised how big it was inside. Probably not quite as big as it was on the outside, but close. It makes me wonder how people can get through so many pairs of shoes. They must be selling them to centipedes. Hundreds and hundreds of shelving units stacked full of them, and rows and rows of conveyor belts adding even more by the second. Nothing very stylish though. Imitation plastic uppers, and MDF soles. A choice of black or brown. And no trainers. I think I'll carry on getting mine through our Tange. She has a knack of grabbing real bargains from the shops. She waits until the big January sales, and then nicks quite a few pairs in the chaos.

I was met by some bloke in a bright yellow jacket, hard-hat, goggles, ear-defenders, boots and gloves. He looked like he'd just come from Iraq. He said his name was Brian, Health & Safety Manager and the nearest qualified first-aider. He was also the nearest twat. He said, in fact he shouted, that he needed to get me kitted out with PPE and inducted, whatever that meant. It sounded more like something the hospital might do if you're pregnant. He asked for my shoe size and head measurement, so I thought I was going to get a few staff freebies. I didn't know they did hats as well though.

He pointed out that in the event of an emergency my nearest exit was the door, which I thought was a bit obvious, and then he started going through some sort of PowerSocket presentation on his computer, which bored the tits off me. I drifted off so I can't remember much about it, except my ears pricked up when he said something about drugs and alcohol. That might have been to do with the menu at the staff canteen.

Anyway, it went on for about forty-five minutes. How people at work ever get any work done is beyond me.

Finally, he dressed me up ready to go to Iraq as well, and led me to the factory floor, where a bloke called Derek started the training. I think he was the boss. It was hard to tell through the face mask and goggles, but I thought I'd seen his picture on the notice board in reception. It was at this point I was going to go faint, but I thought I'd wait to see what they had in store for me first.

Derek showed me a shoe box, and a pair of shoes. He put the shoes into the shoe box, one at a time, while explaining that he was putting the shoes into the shoe box, one at a time. I suppose they have to do that these days to cater for deaf or blind workers. Then he passed the box down the line to a woman called Brenda, who applied the lid.

He asked if I had any questions.

"Why can't I do the lids?" I asked.

"Why?" he said.

"Because it looks a bit easier."

Brenda looked a bit offended, but I thought it was a fair point. It seemed a bit daft to put a newcomer on the skilled part of the job.

"Brenda here has been doing lids for over twenty years," Derek replied after a big sigh. "We value her expertise."

Then Brenda chimed in, silly cow. "It's not just the lids, Doreen. I then have to pass the box down the line to Despatch, ready for despatch."

I suppose that's what happens to people when they've been doing lids for twenty years. It addles the brain. Anyway, it all seemed to be getting a bit complicated, and I started to feel faint. I decided to get some final facts before I keeled over, so I asked Derek what my holiday entitlement was.

"Normally sixteen days," he said, which I assumed was monthly. I didn't like the sound of that. On a five-day week it still meant that I'd have to be working at least one day a week, which was no better than attending the Job Centre. And the hours were longer, so I don't know how he expected me to be impressed. As I asked more questions he seemed to get more and more flustered. He didn't seem to know how many sick days I was allowed, or even what would happen if I was sick while I was on holiday. Would I get a day off in lieu?

In the end Derek walked off, muttering something about getting the Human Research Manager to come and see me.

Brenda decided to show me the kitchenette area, where she said I could make myself a cup of tea at break times, once I'd filled in the two-page risk assessment form and got Brian to pat-test the plug.

I could feel the blood draining from my head, and I had to sit down. Brenda made me a sweet cup of tea and did all the paperwork. I asked if I could take off the goggles, because they steamed up when I tried to sip the tea. She asked Brian and he said it was too dangerous. I manage to drink tea at home without too many incidents, but at work it's different. In the end I spilled some hot liquid down my leg because I couldn't see the mug through the goggles, and had to be quarantined in the first-aid room while they had a meeting about it.

It was now approaching lunchtime, but Derek still popped his head round the door and suggested we did some work. He'd have been right at home in Victorian days.

So finally, despite my injuries, and after another few seconds of intensive training with a real shoe, they let me loose on the production line.

I gave it my best shot for eight minutes and then I passed out.

CHAPTER THIRTEEN
UNLUCKY FOR SOME

I woke up in a strange place which smelled of TCP and old folk. I thought I must be dreaming, because our Troll was there, stood by the side of me, playing with her mobile. I was on a trolley.

"Where am I?"

"You had a funny turn, mother," Troll replied. "You'm in hospital."

I panicked. "Christ - it ay Stafford is it?"

"No, you'm all right, just lie still."

"Why am I on a trolley?"

"I don't know. Be grateful mother, you'm normally off yer trolley."

"Well, how did you get here?"

"They gid me some compassionate leave from the remedial centre. I've got to go back on Monday. Unless you die - I can have two weeks off then."

She made it sound like the two-week option was her favourite. I tried to find out more, but her phone went off. I could only hear half the conversation.

"They'm just doing some tests, Doris," Troll said. "But they reckon her'll be all right...No, her ay in a ward. It's nice though, her's got her own corridor... No, I wouldn't bother if I was you Doris, it'll cost you eighteen quid to park...Oh, okay then, Doris. Tarra....tarra then, Doris...tarra...tarra...tarra."

"Who was it?"

"Doris. Her said when her's finished her quintuple shift at the factory her'll come and visit you, but I told her not to bother."

"Have they said when I'll be back on my feet?"

"You'll never be back on your feet, mother."

Cheeky cow. "You'll have to get Doris to help you round the house a bit, till I'm well."

"I'll cope, mother."

Just then the doctor turned up with a clipboard. He said all the tests were negative, especially the one for excess adrenalin, so they thought I'd just had a bit of a panic attack.

"Any idea what could have caused it?" he asked.

Clearly he'd never worked in a shoe factory. Them junior doctors wouldn't know what a hard day's work looked like. Then came the bombshell.

"Anyway, Mrs Tipton. I've given you the all-clear. You can go back to work."

All I remember after that was the bleepers going off.

* * *

After a week's total rest and recuperation on full pay, I was told I had to report back to the shoe factory for duties. But this time it wasn't really such a problem for me. I'd now had time to plan a proper strategy, and I eventually went back refreshed and ready for work the following Tuesday.

The following day, on the Wednesday back at the Job Centre, the smarmy counsellor was suspicious.

"Did you deliberately get sacked? Because if you did, it's very serious."

It turns out that I'd accidentally put two left shoes in each box, and it cost the company three thousand pounds in returned orders.

To me it looked like constructive dismissal. At no point did the manager ever mention that they had to be a matching pair. They didn't train me right. I had a word with the union rep and decided to take them to an industrious tribunal. Not only was I denied a flexible working hours lunch break at twenty-past nine, but - and here's the disgraceful part of it - they denied me maternity leave.

I missed out on maternity leave when I was having my kids, on account of me not being in work at the time, so I thought it was only right that I took it now that I'd been given a job. But they got rid of me instead, and it was obvious why. I was a woman, and they just didn't want to pay up.

The union rep also argued that it was illegal for the company to discriminate against me on the grounds of ability or enthusiasm. He said that it was a blatant broach of my humane rights, and that I could be entitled to constipation.

In the end the union took my case to the European Court, and they agreed with me.

It was a shame it had to end like that with the shoe factory, after I'd given them nearly two hours of loyal service, and the camaraderie of the workplace is something I'll miss in retirement. The factory boss did try to offer me an out-of-court settlement. He said he'd give me £500 if I went to work for one of his competitors for an hour.

An hour's work for £500? He'd got no chance.

As it turned out, my stint at the shoe factory was the first and last time I ever worked. Nevertheless, the hands-on experience I gained on the shop-floor was far from wasted.

You'll find out why in the final part of my story.

PART FOUR

A LIGHT AT THE END OF THE FUNNEL

CHAPTER FOURTEEN
LIVING THE DREAM

Despite having to grow up in extreme poverty, I never lost my ambition. Every week I would buy twenty-five assorted scratchcards, any one of which could have landed me the biggie.

Looking back, I think I've always had the same instinct to make my own way in the world. When I was a young kid, before the lottery came along, it was the lucky bags. Some of the younger ones amongst you probably wouldn't remember these, but as a child in the early seventies they were your biggest chance of hitting the jackpot, and I insisted that mother got me at least three a day. With a lucky bag, as the name suggested, you got lucky every time - not just with a collection of sweets, but with a surprise plastic toy. It was a long time ago, but my memory is that these were all quality items, and of course it's easy to get hooked when every single one was a winner.

But all too soon the child grows into an adult, and you begin to realize that a two-inch tall plastic man with articulated limbs isn't going to pay the bills - cut the lawn perhaps, because Bernard is very short with plastic hips and could easily have come from a lucky bag - but not pay the bills. So then I graduated on to the scratchcards.

I did the normal lottery as well, of course, but the scratchcards have always been my favourite. I enjoy that fact that there's an extra physical dimension to winning. Somehow, just sitting back and waiting for your numbers to be drawn out of a machine seems a bit lazy.

In the early days, all I managed to win was some Fairy Liquid, but that's no use in the dish washer, and a voucher for 50p off a pair of gardening gloves. I sold that to Bernard for a pound, reinvested the proceeds into another scratchcard, and then lost the lot. But I genuinely believed that one day it would happen, and I knew that if it did you wouldn't see me for dust.

Don't get me wrong, I've got nothing against the Black Country specifically, although some parts of it are a bit depressing. But the way I saw it, if I won a few million, I could afford an interpreter, so there'd be no need to stop round here.

My dream was always to move a bit closer to the Job Centre - not the normal one here by me, one a bit posher, possibly somewhere in Birmingham, like James Turner Street. Some people reading this might think it strange that I'd still sign on if I won a couple of million, but for me it was a point of principle. I can't stand these people who get rich and then forget their roots.

So yes, I'd still do my bit, you know, and claim the welfare, but it would be nice if I could live a bit closer to the office, so I could have a lie-in every now and then, and not have to miss breakfast. That long-haired bloke out of The Beatles, John Lenin, he summed it up nicely:

"Yes, you may think I'm a dreamer, but I'm not the only one." And I wasn't.

Lots of people did the lottery. But somebody had to win it, and I saw no reason why it couldn't be me, and twenty-five reasons a week why it should.

It's even right there on the official advertising: *Pick your numbers, and start dreaming.* So I did. I saw every scratchcard, every Thunderball, every Lotto HotPick as an investment in my future.

I've had a go with pretty much all the different scratchcard games in my time, all seven hundred of them, so I'm probably considered a bit of an expert locally.

I've never done the NHS health lottery though, just on a point of principle. The way I saw it, they've kept me waiting long enough over the years, so I decided that I'd keep the buggers waiting a long time before they saw any of my money. That might seem a bit harsh, but you have to realize that I've been a damn good customer to the NHS over many decades, and stayed loyal to them when I could have gone private, so I don't owe them a penny. You're also never sure with those schemes where the money ends up - how many managers and pen-pushers are skimming it off the top before it gets to the doctors? If I ran the NHS lottery I'd have a different system, which would cut out the middle-man. Imagine the excitement of scratching off the panel and finding you'd won, like, a hip operation, a heart by-pass, or some antibiotics. And yes, I know what you're going to say, but I've thought it through.

Even if you didn't need the thing you'd won - let's say for example that you won an appendix operation and you'd already had yours out - you could still do swaps with somebody else who had won what you wanted, or you could auction it off to the highest bidder and make quite a few quid. And the one who buys it then gets to jump the queue, which in turn encourages those that didn't buy scratchcards to buy some and bring in more money for the NHS, so it's another win-win.

Doris says I should be in Government with ideas like that, and you can see her point. It'd be a lot fairer for everybody, and it would stop that health tourism scandal at a stroke. Foreigners would have to buy their own scratchcards and take pot luck, or make a bid for one of my winning cards, so either way they'd be making a proper contribution to the economy. And imagine how much an emergency life-saving operation or organ transplant scratchcard could fetch? The chances of you needing it yourself would be low, so once that went on eBay it would be as good as winning the biggie.

I think the scratchcard idea could also be rolled out to welfare generally. The Government knows how much people on welfare like scratchcards, so why don't they hand them out to the claimants instead of cash? Instead of paying the housing benefit directly, which is boring, you could have a month's rent as one of the prizes, or some child benefit, or a week's free jobseekers, and then have lots of smaller prizes of things like multi-packs of crisps, or Pringles, and lucky bags for the kids. It would also be a great way for Government to control welfare spending, so that none of it is wasted on gambling.

The other thing that my idea would do is encourage welfare claimants to be a bit more business-minded and entrepioneerial. Here's just one example, which I don't mind sharing with you because I can't really see the Government bringing in the scheme. If I was to win a month's free housing benefit on the welfare lottery, the first thing I'd do is sell it to a family with eight kids living in central London, where it's bound to be worth thousands, rather than use it myself.

Doris says I've got a good head for business, and that one day I should set myself up and become a self-made man. But to be honest I don't want the hassle. I'd much rather act as a consultant from the comfort of my own sofa. I do reckon, though, that politicians should be forced to spend a bit more time sitting on sofas. Sometimes they're just too close to things and can't see the bigger picture, whereas from where I'm sat it's much easier to spot solutions. Like I say, they're just not in touch with ordinary working folk.

Between us, me and Doris have sorted out a whole range of issues over the years, including some world conflicts that have foxed the ones in power. If they'd have just taken the trouble to ask me or Doris, there wouldn't be any more problems in the Middle East, there'd be no poverty in Africa, the Scots wouldn't be revolting, and the Vietnam War would have only lasted a weekend. And all done with scratchcards. So having heard all that, it may surprise you to learn that the next twist in my tale had nothing to do with the lottery.

I've never been much of a one for religion, or for going to church. Sunday was my day of rest, and it would take something special to get me out of the house on the Sabbath. But it does make you wonder about stuff like that when your life is suddenly turned around like magic.

I remembered what the priest said to me once, that God moves in a mischievous way. Well, he was certainly being a crafty little bugger that particular afternoon.

I didn't know it at the time, but things were about to turn round for me in the most extraordinary fashion.

But it wouldn't be down to one of my scratchcards.

A silly idea from one of the kids, messing about with the computer, was about to change my life forever.

CHAPTER FIFTEEN
GOING VIRAL

The YouTube clip was all just an accident, but it ended up changing my life.

Tange had popped back from her bus pass travels for a brief visit, and arrived clutching a massive bag of washing. Honestly, sometimes I despair with kids. It's just not fair on Doris. Anyway, Tange had stolen a video camera from Currys (well, two I suppose, if you count the security camera) and she wanted to test it out. She sat me down on the sofa - no actually, come to think of it, I might have already been on the sofa - anyway, she asked me just to talk, and I said, "What about?" and she said, "Just anything. Just talk about yourself."

So I started wittering on about my syndrome, and

my kids, the state of the nation, and whatever. Next thing I knew, Tange had put it on the computer and folks from all over the world were looking at it and making all sorts of comments, not all of them nice. 'Doreen's Story' she'd called it. By the time she looked the next day it had over a million hits, and I started getting calls from the newspapers.

The Sunday Times wanted to do an interview. So did the Birmingham Post, the Sunday Mercury, Free Radio - they was all at it.

Then about a week later I had Channel Four on the phone. They said they wanted to make one of them Fly-Up-The-Wall documentaries about me, a bit like that Benefits Street. Of course, I was wary.

Don't get me wrong, I've got nothing against Benefits Street. That White Dee's a proper character. She must have claimed she was poor, presumably, as she was on benefits, but from what I could see she wasn't short of food. And then look what happened. They gave her a makeover, and they kept putting her on Breakfast telly. That's probably it. Perhaps she had too many breakfasts. And then they even tried to make her into a rap singer. Good luck with that, love. Well, let's be honest, she's the wrong colour for rapping. White Dee - there's a bit of a clue in the name. We just haven't got the rhythm, us white folk.

I had a go at singing last Christmas, when the kids got hold of one of them hokey cokey machines. But I couldn't take to it, so I put it in the car boot.

My only gripe with Benefits Street is that it tried to show people like me in a bad light.

I know, because I've been behind the scenes in one of these fly-up-the-wall documentaries myself, and I know how it works. It's all in the editing, you see. They'm clever how they twist things. So if you see a character saying something like "Let's go and rob that van…" well, in reality, he probably didn't say that. He probably said, "Let's go and help that old lady over the road." But they twist it, see, to make him look bad. That's how it works.

Them cigarettes and lager cans in their hands? All painted on afterwards. And all the swear words, apparently, are dubbed on after by rappers - and I mean proper bloody rappers, not White Dee.

But Benefits Street, if you ask me, is actually a nice little community. They've got Winson Green prison right on the doorstep, which is convenient. They do their own recycling, judging by the amount of mattresses on the pavement. And look at all the charity work they do. There's no charge for house clearances. And one week they even entered that Britain In Bloomers competition, and they did all right. They come eighth in the area, I think. Out of about six. They asked us to do that in our street, but I can't cope with the gardening. Not with my knees. My crucial ligaments have gone. I need something a bit more low maintenance. That's why I asked the council to concrete over my window box.

Okay, all the characters in Benefits Street seemed a bit larger than life, but that's probably down to the size of my plasma. But there's also a real sense of community. They'll do anything for you - cook you some soup, get you a scratchcard, advise you on your humane rights, sell you some crack. In a small community, that's worth more than money. Well, it is around here. The crack I mean.

Obviously, like in any community, there's always going to be one or two bad eggs spoiling the bunch of apples, but they shouldn't tarnish them all with the same paintbrush. All most of them want to do is to come home, after a hard day sitting on the front doorstep, and earn an honest day's benefits. And for them that does want to do a bit better for themselves, well, good luck to them.

The foreigners on Benefits Street worried me a bit though. All they seemed interested in was finding a job, and we don't want them setting a bad example in front of our kids. I mean, most of them seemed to be from Romania, but there was, like, eighty-four of them in the one room, which is a bit much.

But there again, that's not really their fault. It's the Government's fault, because nobody can afford bedrooms any more, thanks to that bedroom tax. There was a bloke on the news the other day; he was an irate tax payer, I think they said, so apparently he had to give 40% of his bedroom to the taxman. And it was the bit with the fitted wardrobes in, so he couldn't get ready in a morning to go to work. They just don't think it through do they?

Luckily, I managed to get round that bedroom tax. I've had my spare room converted into a Mosque, accessed by a ramp.

Anyway, where was I?

Oh, yes. The YouTube clip.

Well, the thing was, the video just started getting more and more hits - it was over one and a half million now. It was being talked about in America, Smethwick and all over the world. Then folks started arguing about the politics of it - lefties, righties, Nazis, Brummies, Yam-Yams - all calling each other all sorts. And in the middle of all that I was starting to get a bit famous.

People kept stopping me at the scratchcard counter and saying, "Am yo that Doreen from the YouTube clip?" And I was.

And the more it went on, the more it occurred to me that I could become the next White Dee, and end up on Celebrity Big Brother and make a few quid.

But there was a big difference.

Whereas that White Dee's just an actress, playing a part on the telly, I'm a real person, so that made me a bit more bony fido.

It wasn't just about the telly either. Some theatre producer chap who'd been keeping an eye on the YouTube success decided it would be a good idea to do a tour of local theatres. He reckoned that people would buy tickets, and he assured me it wouldn't involve any work. Within a few weeks he'd devised the show and called it *An Audience With Doreen*. The priest popped round again and he told me that the Pope did something similar, so he encouraged me to give it a go.

I never quite understood how it all worked, but they put a sofa on the stage for me, and set Doris up with an ironing board next to me, and asked us just to chat away about our life and our opinions.

To our amazement, they sold the tickets, every single one of them, across over twenty nights. And everywhere we went folk came up afterwards and wanted their photos taking with me so they could post them on Faceache. It was all very bewildering.

I've put some of the photos at the end of this book for you to see. They seemed to be treating me like some sort of hero. Well, I don't know about that. Heroin perhaps, that's something I'm more used to, but it was lovely all the same.

So, bit by bit, things seemed to be turning around for me.

But my ambitions to be rich and famous were about to be put on hold by a sudden tragic incident in the family, and things would never be the same again.

CHAPTER SIXTEEN
MIRIAM POPS HER CLOGS

At first, it was just like any other Thursday.

Miriam had rung to say she'd missed her buzz, and she'd be a bit late. When she finally arrived she was froze to jeth, so I got Doris to give her a cup of tea and a piece of cake. You might remember me saying that Doris had once pointed out that my fruit cake, the one I'd bought from the corner shop, was past its sell-by date by about ten years.

Well, this was that day.

Our Miriam still tucked into the cake in the usual way, though - half of it ending up in her mouth, and the other half on the carpet in crumbs. I could see Doris rolling her eyes at the thought of her having to get the hoover out again.

Now, I know that some of you out there who watch too much of that CSI Miami on telly might already be jumping to conclusions, thinking that it was the out-of-date cake that killed her, and that I should be arrested on a charge of gulpable homicide.

Hold your horses. First of all, I'd only had the cake a couple of years, in which case it would have been the corner shop's fault not mine, and secondly, there was the blow to the head.

I was having them solar plexus panels fitted on the roof at the time, and one of the blokes who'd come in to ask if he could get up my loft-hole managed to catch our Miriam on the head with the ladder when he turned round. Now, to my eyes, it didn't look very much, and Miriam had only lost consciousness for a few minutes. And, to be fair to the bloke with the ladder, after that she seemed to be as right as rain again, up to the point where she died. But as Doris pointed out later, even a tap on the head when you're ninety-one could be like a mallet to you and me.

Anyway, the fact remains that Miriam and me both fell asleep that afternoon watching Jeremy Kyle, and when we woke up she was dead.

At first, I thought she was just too deaf to hear me trying to wake her, even with the megaphone on full blast. That's when I shook her hand and noticed how cold she was. Doris had heard my scream even from next-door, and came running round to see what had happened. She thought I'd been offered another job.

After sedating me with some brandy, Doris phoned for the doctor, and put the kettle on. I covered up Miriam's face with a tea-towel as a mark of respect.

The doctor arrived about half an hour later. He confirmed that Miriam had indeed passed away, and then he called for an ambulance, though personally I thought it was a bit late for that.

He explained that they had to get her to hospital in case they wanted to do a post-mortem. Apparently the best time to do that is after somebody's died.

The doctor could see how distressed we were, so he asked if I wanted him to wheel Miriam out of the lounge and off somewhere else while he waited for the ambulance. I told him there was a freezer in the garage. I tend not to use it much - I think there were some old sausages in there, but he could chuck those out. They probably had hoss-meat in them anyway. But he said the ambulance wasn't going to be that long, so he just put her in the hall for a bit.

Doris was all of a lather, and even reached for the brandy herself. "If the post-mortem mentions fruit cake, we'm both up on a murder charge," she said in a panicky whisper while the doctor was in the hall.

I tried to put her mind at rest by reminding her that it wouldn't be both of us. She was the one who'd noticed the date, and she was the one who'd given the cake to Miriam, so she could leave me out of it.

We had a few sleepless nights after that. Well, Doris did. But in the end, the post-mortem verdict was that Miriam had died from boredom, so we both breathed a big sigh of relief.

Miriam Bertha Agnes Mildred Potter was buried a fortnight later, on her ninety-second birthday, and I knew that Thursdays would never be the same again. Especially for her.

Now, I said earlier that our Miriam would turn out to play a big part in my story. So you might be wondering how that's possible, now that she's dead.

Well, every week, rain or shine, Miriam did the Euromillions lottery. And that Thursday, the day she died, she was still clutching her ticket. I noticed it sticking out of her hand while I was covering her up with the tea-towel.

At the time, I just decided it was best for me to look after it for her, in case she revived, because otherwise she might have dropped it somewhere in the ambulance. But, when it became clear that our Miriam was never coming back, I decided to check the numbers in the free paper.

The thing was, you see, Miriam always used the same numbers, week in, week out. 1, 2, 3, 4, 5, with lucky stars 6 and 7.

Her memory wasn't very good of late, so she liked to keep it simple. Well, I suppose those numbers had as good a chance of winning as any other numbers, but somehow I couldn't see anybody else choosing them, so the moment they came up, I knew Miriam had hit the biggie.

It was a triple rollover week, and nobody would be sharing the money. So that's how I ended up with a hundred and sixty-one million, and a bit of loose change.

I was the only family she'd got, so I knew Miriam would have wanted me to have it. Nevertheless, I decided not to tell anybody else just yet where I'd found the ticket, not till the money was in my bank.

You never know with these crafty lawyers, they'd be swarming all over it like vultures. Death duties, inheritance tax, whatever. There was no way they were getting their hands on our Miriam's money, so I saw myself as her legal guardian. I didn't even let on to Doris.

As it happens, I did the right thing. It turns out that our Miriam had made a will, and left everything she had to the local cat rescue centre. What a bloody waste that would have been.

Nevertheless, I still felt morally obliged to honour Miriam's dying wishes in some way, so I made a point of buying a cat, and donating it to the rescue centre in her memory.

I even called it Miriam.

It's what she would have wanted.

CHAPTER SEVENTEEN
ALL'S WELL

Every Thursday I still raise a glass with Doris to toast our Miriam, at the exact time she passed away.

No more stout or brandy for me though, it's just champagne now. It goes right to Doris's head. She goes all giggly, and once that happens I know I'm not going to get any more sensible work out of her that day. But age has mellowed me, and I'm a far more relaxed employer these days, so I usually let her go home early to sleep it off.

I bought myself a new house. Well, actually, not quite bought. My financial adviser got me to set up a limited company, with him as one of the Directors. The company rents me the house, so should I ever go off me head, the council can't come and have it to pay for my care.

It's in a posh area - in a side street just around the corner from the Job Centre. And true to my word, I still go every Wednesday. Not to sign on, though. In the end all the publicity about the lottery win made that too hard.

These days, I go to keep them informed about any vacancies I might have in my shoe factory.

Yes, Doreen Limited bought that as well. And it's doing all right. The machine for packing is mended, and we've just launched a new range of own-brand fluffy trainers which double as slippers, so you can wear them day and night. We call them Trippers, and they're very popular around here. We even export now to Birmingham, and some parts of Coventry. So, I'm doing my bit for the economy and employing fifty people, with plans to take on more next month.

I always make a point of interviewing the new employees myself, just to make sure they really want the job. I know what it's like being on the other side of that desk.

There's no doubt that having a bit of money has made things easier for me. I've had a stairlift put in, and one of them airport travelators for the hallway. I also bought an indoor motorized hammock, and a new recliner sofa with a built-in fridge.

But apart from that, things are much the same. I still have my online grocery delivery, but it's now charged to my own name. Troll sorted it out for me, on her computer at the remedial centre. The bloke whose account she originally hacked into must have changed his password. No more takeaways for me either. The Chef sees to that.

And I finally got around to having one of them 3D tellies, which is amazing - it feels like you're right in there, sitting next to Jeremy Kyle. I'm going to send off for a Blu-ray of The Railway Kids next, and a box of tissues.

I don't even mind paying bail so much these days. Anything to see the kids now and again. It's not easy trying to coordinate the various release dates so we can all get together as a family again, but when we do I've promised them we'll have the best Christmas ever. Talking of which, Christ knows how much washing they'll bring back after all these years, but I'm sure Doris will cope somehow.

And of course, being a grandmother brings its own responsibilities. I sometimes offer to babysit on a Wednesday evening for Trojan's kids, as she's away such a lot on business. I don't think it's healthy for them being with the authorities all the time, and it gives the social workers a break.

It's a bit tiring for me after a trip to the Job Centre, but Wednesday's the only day Doris can do.

Kids grow up so fast. Taser's three and a half now, so old enough to look after herself, but we still like to keep an eye on her in case she gets hold of a kitchen knife, or some matches and petrol from the shed like last time.

Then there's little Tyson. He's only just turned five, but already showing every sign of following in the footsteps of his hero, Mike.

And finally there's Tyson's twin sister, Tantrum, who's a couple of weeks older than her brother. It was a difficult birth. I think Trojan named her after Ryan O'Neill's daughter, on account of her being such a drama queen. She's a proper little madam, but it's nothing a bit of Gaffer tape can't sort. These days I can also afford to bring in my own private security guard, who's ex-military, so I don't think there's any danger to the public.

Tange and Troll, on the other hand, never bothered with kids - in fact they never bothered with men generally. There have been a few boyfriends in the past, but they never lasted very long. I think the longest one was seven minutes, unless you count the fifteen-minute wait for the ambulance. He's up and about now though, and walking with the aid of a stick. I reckon the girls just prefer their own space.

There's no doubt that it makes you reflect as you pass some of the great millstones in your life. I've got a big birthday coming up, and I've been trying to decide how to commenstruate it in the most fitting way. One idea I came up with was to have a proper family portrait done - me, the kids, the grand-kids, all Photoshopped together like we're in the same room - and then have it tastefully tattooed onto my stomach to cover up the Bavarian section scars. There's a place in Bilston that does it, apparently. A woman at the Job Centre recommended it to me after she'd had her God-daughter tattooed on her thigh. They'd spelt her name wrong, but she was delighted with it, and I wasn't going to have any writing on mine so that doesn't matter.

I thought it was a lovely idea, and I was all set to do it, until Doris pointed out that tattooing hurts, and at the very least I should have the black midwife on hand. She also said that it might not be a good idea to have something as permanent as a tattoo done, just in case I ever fell out with one of the kids. She's got a wise head on her, that one. But to top it all she then came up with her 'piece of resistance' - an alternative idea that was pure genius. She suggested that I had the family portrait turned into one of them iron-on transfers instead, and she could put it on a tea-towel for me. As an extra special touch, she said she could iron it onto the same tea towel that I used to cover up Miriam's head when she died, so it would also act as a nice momentum of her life.

I've said it before and I'll say it again, I really don't know what I'd do without Doris.

A new house, a factory, grand-kids, a bit of money behind me - yes, my life has certainly changed a lot since the windfall.

The biggest difference of all, though, is with the scratchcards. I now have five hundred a week, so it must be only a matter of time before I win the biggie. Scratching them all is very time-consuming, but I've never shirked when it comes to things like that. There's no way I'd employ somebody else to do it for me. It would be too easy for them to cheat and pinch the winning card.

I enjoy it though. I see myself as a bit like the early prospectors in America, panning for gold. I'm currently stockpiling Fairy Liquid and gardening gloves, but I know my luck will change.

But if there's one thing I've learned on my journey through life, it's that no matter how much money you've got, you still need good neighbours. And they don't come any better than Doris. So, in order to hang on to her services, I had to buy her the house next door to mine.

None of us are getting any younger, so I made sure Doris no longer does any shifts in the factory. These are big houses, and doing the housework for two of them is a full-time job in itself. It probably takes her a good fifteen minutes a day just to shovel and bag up the pile of metal scratchcard scrapings from by the sofa, and hoover all the bits.

At least I've got her the proper tools for the job now though - one of them new high-fangled vacuum cleaners with anti-cycledrome technology and no dust-bags to empty. "The suction's amazing," she says. "It fetches birds out of the sky." Let's hope she makes the most of it before the EU bans them. I like to see Doris enjoying her work. I had her a special sweatshirt made saying *Wonder Woman*. She liked that.

Jack's semi-retired now as well. No more hands-on work anyway. I set him up with his own plumbing business, and he has a staff of twelve under him. All Polish.

They're good workers, he says. He wouldn't touch the British plumbers with a barge-pole, if Pole's the word I want.

Jack also doubles as my chauffeur. I even got him

a proper professional uniform from the fancy-dress shop. He's a good, steady driver, Jack. And he can save up to eleven percent of fuel by driving at exactly fifty-six miles an hour, dependent of course on the nature of the terrain.

*   *   *

It's easy to look back with eyesight and think I could have done things differently. But, at the end of the day, I know I can look people straight in the horse's mouth and say with a clear consciousness that I, Doreen Tipton, followed my dream.

Yes, I know the cynics among you could argue that winning the Euromillions lottery jackpot, especially with a ticket I didn't even buy, might have involved an element of luck.

But there's an old saying in the Black Country: 'The harder you work, the luckier you get.'

Take it from me. That's bollocks.

Thank you for supporting Doreen.

Your purchase of this book will go a long way towards making you slightly poorer.

And now, a few photos…

I've never been a morning person, and I once had to make an appearance on the breakfast show at Free Radio.

Jackie Vale is just one of the lovely people that came and sat with me on the sofa when we did our stage show:
"An Audience With Doreen"

Here are some more…

Andy Johnson   …and Gail Goode

More sofa guests…

Me and Troll (far left) with Joanne Timmins, and somebody called Darren Haywood, who's just the spit of that bloke up the Job Centre…

Me and Troll again, this time with John Penlington. He's asking me who that strange bloke is with the short trousers.

Me with Lee Murphy & Friends, and that strange bloke
again. I think he must be a stalker.

Me and Zita Thomas. Sisters unite.

This is me with Emma and Lois Tristram, the kids of that ghost-writer. They've got attitude.

Me and our Miriam (before she died). I'm not sure why Doris isn't at the ironing board. She was probably slacking.

Doris is back at her station, talking for England. No wonder she never gets anything done. Our Troll is messing about with unsociable media.

Bernard comes round to do my garden about once a week. He's older than God's dog.

Bernard usually offers to trim my bush, but to be honest I prefer Doris to wax it.

On holiday with Doris and Jack in their caravan in Wales. I don't know who took the picture. It was raining.

Our Troll admiring the telly in the caravan.

The smarmy Job Centre bloke.

After I earned a few bob on the lottery, I decided to treat myself to a new taxi.

An old school friend of mine, Gill Jordan.
I think she's just been watching me on the telly.